APOLLO AT GO

A novel that dramatizes the realistic story of NASA's moon shot. The author shows how the three astronauts "sweat out" their selection, then what they experience on their flight, and the thrill and suspense of their actual landing on the moon.

APOLLO AT GO

By Jeff Sutton

G. P. PUTNAM'S SONS • NEW YORK

APOLLO AT GO

To my wife, Eugenia, who copiloted this flight on the typewriter.

Chapter 1

Blood pressure 120/80.
Pulse 72.
Respiration 13.
This was it. Lt. Col. Joseph Faulk, USMC, knew it. He kept his lean face expressionless, his dark eyes on Doctor Ashfield. Not from anything the doc had said, he realized—that would be up to Phil Herndon, the administrator—but rather from his general demeanor. Ashfield was too grave, his aging eyes too critical. Besides, selection of the three-man crew to man the Apollo space vehicle on the first lunar landing attempt was overdue, with the launching less than two weeks away. For weeks "Guess the Crew" had been a favorite pastime of reporters and columnists, with every conceivable combination being chosen from among the eleven astronauts who comprised the National Aeronautics and Space Administration's Space Team One. Now the huge three-stage Saturn C-5 booster, atop which Apollo rode, was on the pad undergoing the final tests and checkout.

Himself? He let the hope unfold and almost as quickly squelched it. Not after the debacle of two years ago, he bitterly reflected. His name only occasionally appeared prominently in the national

guessing game. The physical exam would be taken by the entire
first team—a weeding out. Still, he discerned a difference in the
doctor's manner. He kept his face wooden, and wondered if the
other knew the tumult within him.

The doctor straightened abruptly, letting his stethoscope dangle.
"Fit as a fiddle, Joe. How do you feel about the flight?"

There, it was out. Faulk exhaled slowly. "I'm hoping."

"Praying," Ashfield corrected. Slight and graying, his eyes probed
the astronaut through gold-rimmed glasses.

"That too," Faulk admitted. He waited for the other to mention
the strike—the big strike against him—relieved when he didn't.
Instead Ashfield asked, "Karen?"

"She's game." A vision of his wife flashed through Faulk's mind
—a blond girl with a girlish figure despite the two children she had
borne him, her brave smile when they discussed the possibility of
his selection. Not that either of them expected he would get it—
not after the launch he had aborted. Yet he knew her smile masked
a thousand fears. Karen wouldn't show them. She'd never show
them. She'd sweated out a thousand jet flights in almost nameless
corners of the globe. Only at night, when she trembled in her sleep,
did he discern the real depths of her fears.

Ashfield nodded absently. "She's game." His tone said that he
understood Karen Faulk perfectly, knew all about the fears she
hid behind her slightly crooked smile. "You're hep on going, eh?"
he ended.

Faulk suppressed his jubilation. The question was tantamount
to admitting he was under serious consideration. At the same time
he weighed the question carefully. Ashfield, an M.D., also happened to be a psychiatrist—a very good one. Faulk felt he knew
him quite intimately, or as intimately as one could know the thin,
graying man who was both physician and father-confessor to the
astronauts of Space Team One, the chosen candidates for deep space
flight. In the final analysis, he knew, Ashfield walked a lonely is-

land. Yet Faulk believed himself closer to the physician than the others. Because they swapped yarns together over an occasional beer? Because Ashfield frequently dropped by the house? He didn't know; but he did understand that the routine physical he'd just undergone was a subterfuge to allow Ashfield to ask the very questions he was asking now. The answers were critical.

Faulk caught the expectancy in the physician's face and said, "It's my job . . . what I've been trained for."

"So have the others."

"Yes," he agreed calmly.

"But you want to go?"

"Of course."

"Self-glory, Joe?"

"Perhaps, I don't know." He met the other's eyes. "Why did Hillary want to scale Everest? The question goes back to the dawn of time, Doc. The answer's the same."

"Which is?"

"Because it's there."

"So it is self-glory?"

"Human curiosity," Faulk amended, "but I can't argue motives with you. I suppose there are roots."

"Deep roots, Joe. Feel confident?"

"If you're thinking—"

"I'm not thinking anything," the physician cut in. "It's a logical question."

Faulk said defensively, "I feel very confident."

"In Apollo or in yourself?"

"Both." He hesitated. "You can't separate the crew from the spacecraft. It's a team."

"It's that," Ashfield acknowledged. He leaned back, scrutinizing him bemusedly. "You all give the same answers, Joe. Have you rehearsed them?"

"Negative." Faulk grinned, amused despite his tension. This was

Ashfield the psychiatrist talking, trying to bait him. A favorite probing tool. "Isn't it natural we think alike?"

Ashfield chuckled. "I suppose, but I'd still like to know how you really feel. Any fear?" The last question came like a bullet.

"There's always fear in this business," he acknowledged obliquely. "It's part of it. You know that. Any pilot who's ever climbed into a jet feels the same."

"More now than when you were with the jets?"

"I'd say so."

"How do you account for that?"

"In a plane you're responsible all the way, from wheels up to wheels down," Faulk explained. "Here, during boost phase, I'm just so much baggage."

"At the mercy of the machine, eh?"

"Something like that."

"A normal reaction," Ashfield acceded.

Faulk grinned. "You should try it, Doc."

"No thanks, I'll stick to the pill routine." He leaned forward slightly. "Who do you think is the top pilot of Space Team One, Joe? Yourself excepted."

Faulk hesitated, caught by surprise. "A toss-up," he said finally. "Max Kovac or Whitey Burke."

"Interesting." Ashfield glanced at his watch. "That should do it, Joe."

"Thanks." As Faulk rose, the physician peered up at him.

"Send Kovac over, will you?"

"Will do." Capping his excitement, he left the office. The moon. The Big Jump. The goal he'd been aiming for since that long-ago time when a Sputnik had whizzed over the earth, its beeps alerting mankind to the dawn of a new age. For a while everything had been rosy. He'd come up fast, had been the number one astronaut. Until . . .

He pushed the painful memory from mind. He had a chance, a

slim one. Why Ashfield's last question? To get his opinion . . .
weigh his judgment? Kovac and Burke were tops. That was generally conceded, even if he did believe himself to be better. It would
be Kovac, he thought, or Burke. Or both. That left the number
three spot. It depended on Ashfield, his evaluation. And on Phil
Herndon, the administrator. But if he knew Ashfield, he didn't
know Herndon. The latter was tough, a rock, a man to whom senti-
ment was an alien word. Herndon's god was Apollo, his goal the
moon. Ashfield could pass on their physical and mental readiness;
Herndon would have a single criterion: *Has he got what it takes?*
Pass that test, he reflected, and the administrator wouldn't care if
he had two heads.

Later he went outside, staring toward Complex 39, the huge
NASA launching site erected for but one purpose—to hurl men to
the moon. The gargantuan truss-steel gantry cut a notch in the sky,
appearing as peaceful in the westering sun as a silo brooding over
a Midwest wheat field. Within the belly of the gantry was Saturn,
the huge three-stage booster that would push Apollo into earth orbit on its first leg to the moon. There, too, was a strange craft
known officially as the Lunar Excursion Module but more popularly called the Moon Bug, which would act as a ferry between the
moon-orbiting Apollo and the bleak lunar surface. The Moon Bug,
a ship of dreams. . . . He raised his eyes, gazing at the quarter
crescent now sliding into the west.

The moon. He let the painful memories slip back. The first
prototype Apollo moonships had been tested in suborbital flight to
determine their reentry characteristics. Two years before, such a
launch had been made. Only Apollo had never reached the edge of
space. The shot had been aborted—he had aborted it!

The past rushed back.

T plus 15 seconds. The booster rocket was climbing, gathering
acceleration, commencing pitchover into its programed trajectory.
Apollo rode its nose. He'd piloted that one alone. The copilot and

third crew member had been replaced by ballast. Sitting in the commander's seat, he'd felt the gathering G forces, vibrations shaking the cabin—the harsh, bellowing thunder from the stern tubes. He'd been a tiger in those days—the number one astronaut, his selection to man the moonshot all but a foregone conclusion.

Yes, he remembered.

Up, up, reaching for the sky. Then . . .

The board flashed red.

Fire warning! Riding atop thousands of gallons of highly volatile liquid oxygen/kerosene fuel, he watched the board flash red. He lived the moment again as he had a thousand times since. Red! Danger! Fire! Fuel spilling from a broken line—flames above the afterburner! He tensed, waiting for the automatic abort, and when it didn't come, spoke tersely into the mike:

"Pilot to launch control. I have a red board—fire warning!" He stared at the red light, momentarily expecting the thunderous explosion which would shred the rocket into a million flaming fragments. The radio crackled almost immediately, and through the hellish sound spectrum he heard the word "abort!" He reacted without hesitation as he had been trained to react—he reached forward and yanked the manual abort switch. Instantly a battery of powerful solid-propellant rockets ignited, hurling Apollo free of the booster rocket, thrusting it into the sky with crushing force. Tremendous G's, blackout . . . He came to as the space cabin plopped into the sea. A destroyer picked him up almost immediately.

No red light!

That's what they said at the command post. The instruments had been riding the green right up to the instant he had pulled the abort switch. The booster rocket had gone through its programed flight —a flight that had cost millions and had yielded nothing. Because of him. Launch control had radioed: "No abort indicated." The instruments showed an okay shot, a Green Bird, as they called it.

Later he explained it to a board—the flashing red fire warning, the single twisted word he'd heard on the radio. Everyone was nice to Joe Faulk after that. The board agreed there must have been an instrument malfunction. Aside from Senator Ford Halpern's indignant scream over the wasted millions of dollars, the subject seldom cropped up.

But he had slipped as the number one astronaut. The papers and television stopped referring to him as "the astronaut being groomed for the moonshot." Instead the honor became split between Max Kovac and Whitey Burke. Not that Kovac and Burke weren't good. They were. But Faulk had always prided himself on being the best. *Lt. Col. Joseph Faulk, USMC, the man who aborted the Apollo*— that was the whisper. Professionally, he should have been dead, but he stuck, and Karen backed him all the way. She understood. He'd made four orbital runs since, but as a crew member. Max Kovac or Whitey Burke had held down the pilot's seat. Now, just possibly, he might get a chance. Not as pilot—he held no hope for that—but as the number two or three man. He'd settle for that.

He stared at the gantry, drawing the rocket in his mind. The huge Boeing first stage with its five giant F-1 engines capable of 7.5 million pounds of thrust; the North American second stage with its ring of J-2 engines burning the highly volatile liquid oxygen/liquid hydrogen combination; the Douglas third stage. . . . Atop these would be the Moon Bug, the small vehicle that would break away from Apollo while it circled the moon for descent to the lunar surface. Finally there was the single-engine Apollo itself, a craft designed to carry the astronauts to the moon and back, and while there, whirl in lunar orbit while the Moon Bug wrote its journey into history. If he could see Apollo now, it would look like a speck on Saturn's nose—a fly perched atop a flashlight.

He sensed someone approaching and turning, saw Les Mallon, a lieutenant commander who had come to the astronauts via the carrier *Navy*. Mallon gave a cocky smile and fished for a cigarette.

"A real beaut." He nodded toward the gantry.

"A bird," Faulk agreed. He liked Mallon. Short and wiry, with blond hair and an engaging boyish grin despite his thirty-five years, he was the only bachelor among the astronauts—a state he attributed to his inability to disappoint the rest of the girls. Occasionally he stopped by Faulk's house with a carton of beer to talk over the old days when they'd both flown jets, or brought a date to form a foursome. Les, he'd found, liked the good things in life—music, parties, sailing, loafing on sunny beaches; yet he'd buckled down to the rugged training regimen, handily making the first team. He also had a razor-sharp mind. Faulk had pegged him as a real tiger.

Mallon looked back from the gantry, observing, "We should be hearing."

"Anxious?"

"Nervous as a bride."

"So am I," Faulk admitted.

"No reason to be." Mallon's blue eyes appraised him candidly.

"No?"

"You're a cinch, Joe."

"Yeah," Faulk drawled bitterly, remembering the abort, tasting the gall of it.

"Everyone on the team knows it," the other persisted.

"I don't, Les."

"Bushwa." Mallon faced him. "You're the only one who remembers the past, Joe. Everyone knows it was a malfunction. You're heads up on the rest of us, and look at your orbit time."

"There's more to it than orbit time, Les."

"You've got that too."

He grinned, pleased. "I hope you're right."

"I'm right," Mallon asserted. "The toss-up is for the rest of the crew."

"Any ideas?" Faulk gauged him carefully. Like himself, the navy man kept a sharp ear to the ground. In the past his judgment had proved sound.

"Max Kovac or Whitey Burke," he replied decisively, "but not both. They'll hold one back for the follow-on shot."

"And . . . ?"

"From there on out it's strictly a gamble. I think I have a chance, but so have Waco, Myers, any of the others. It's a toss-up."

"Don't sell yourself short, Les."

"Trying to be honest," he explained. He turned, facing the east. A quarter-moon hung in the sky. "It's a long jump."

"Closer than last year," Faulk responded.

"Very much closer. At times I wonder."

"About what?"

"The moon." Caught by the wistful expression on the other's face, Faulk waited. Mallon spoke slowly: "It's just a big chunk of cratered rock, airless, freezing and boiling by turn, lifeless. Yet it's a magnet."

"A stepping-stone, Les."

"We know it so well," he went on, as if he hadn't heard. "I can't imagine it'll hold many surprises."

"I'm not so certain," Faulk answered, thinking they really didn't know the moon at all. It had been measured, weighed, gridded, examined by instruments. The lonely voices of probes sent to its surface had revealed temperatures, composition, texture. Yet what did they really know? Mighty little, he mused.

"But I want to go," Mallon exclaimed softly.

"We all do."

"Want to go so bad it hurts," he amended. "It's like a spring tight-wound inside me. I want to go, but at times I wonder why."

"We all feel the same, Les."

"A pressure?"

"Sure."

Mallon stared at the moon again, then flipped his cigarette to the ground and stomped on it. "Whaddya say we get a beer?"

many respects Phil Herndon had the toughest job in the
tional Aeronautics and Space Administration. He wasn't the
top—he administrated at a lower level—but he had the final recom-
mendation in the selection of the Apollo crew. Stocky, with thinning gray hair and the arms and shoulders of an athlete going to
fat, he was completely dedicated to his job. He was also conscious
that success or disaster . . . life or death . . . could rest on his
decisions. That's what made his job so tough.

Approaching the administrator's office, Faulk felt a stab of
expectancy, for he regarded the summons as most certainly con-
nected with the selection of the moon crew.

Herndon rose as he entered. Shaking hands briefly, Faulk was
conscious of the other's eyes. Dark and sharp, deep-buried under
heavy orbital ridges, they quickly scrutinized him; as if satisfied
with what he saw, Herndon waved toward a chair and dropped
back behind the desk.

"Looks like you're it, Joe," he said, as soon as Faulk was seated.
Herndon wasn't one to waste words.

"I didn't expect it." He felt a catch in his throat.

Herndon lifted his eyes. "Thinking of the abort, Joe?"

"Yes."

"Those things happen."

"I know." A faint smile touched Faulk's lips. "I was there."

"Malfunction," Herndon said. "Forget it."

"Others haven't," he answered, feeling the pain. "I appreciate
your confidence, Phil, but I don't want to undermine the shot."

"Undermine it how?" Herndon queried softly.

"The men with me. Would they have confidence?"

"Why not?"

"Joe Faulk, who aborted the Apollo—it's a tag stuck to my name,
Phil."

"Unstick it," Herndon said sharply. "I'm dumping this baby in
your lap because I know you can handle it, Joe. If I thought some-

one else better, he'd be the man. We're operating on our best judgment, not hunches. You've been in orbit four times in this rig, and you've turned in a damned good job each time."

"Burke and Kovac were the pilots," he objected.

"They're sold on you, Joe. Now we're asking you to take the big jump."

"I'll do it," Faulk said simply.

"Good." Herndon sat back, relaxing. "You've earned it."

"You could say that for any of them," he replied, thinking of the deep disappointment others would feel when the final crew selection became known. While flight success was paramount, Faulk knew each man hoped to be—if not pilot—at least a member of the three-man crew. Pilot? He looked inquisitively at the administrator. As if reading his thoughts, Herndon said:

"You'll have the number one slot, Joe. It's your bird." Faulk nodded, not trusting himself to speak. "Any questions?" Herndon got a match and lit a battered cherrywood pipe.

"Have the other decisions been made?"

"The crew? No." The administrator contemplated him calmly. "I'm not making that decision, Joe."

"Oh?"

"Ordinarily I would," Herndon continued, "but I think you should pick your own crew. That's a slight edge we can give you. There's one restriction." Faulk waited. "You can't have both Burke and Kovac. We'll have to hold one . . . for the next go."

"I appreciate that."

"I'm not suggesting . . ."

"I know that, Phil. I'd like Kovac."

"Max?" The administrator didn't appear surprised.

"I had either him or Burke pegged for the top slot," Faulk confessed.

"I wrestled with that decision," Herndon admitted. "How about the number three man?"

"Les Mallon," he decided.

"The happy bachelor," Herndon mused. Again he didn't appear surprised. "Does he know there are no women on the moon?"

Faulk smiled. "He'll be happy to make the sacrifice."

"I suppose he can stand it." Herndon's eyes showed a rare twinkle. "You have a team, Joe."

"I appreciate your confidence, Phil."

"We should thank you."

"A million guys would give their eyeteeth to be in my spot," Faulk countered.

"Mostly fools who don't know the risks," Herndon replied soberly. He balanced a pencil between his fingertips, gauging the other thoughtfully. "We've put everything we've got into it, Joe. You know that. But there are still unknowns. Big ones."

"That goes for every new plane that lifts off the ground, Phil."

"Sure, it's relative, but I'm certain you're not underestimating the job."

"You've given me good hardware, Phil, and one doggone good crew."

"The best," Herndon agreed. Fixing his gaze on the far wall, he continued quietly. "This launch is more important than any one man or ten thousand men. It's not merely a case of advancing the technology. This flight will influence foreign policy, our friends and foes. It'll affect our culture, our economics and national psychology. It's been heralded for ten years, Joe. We've staked our national prestige on it."

"I appreciate that, Phil."

"As it is, we're pushing it," Herndon continued. "We'd planned a few moon orbits first, land on the third or fourth flight, but time won't permit."

"I realize that too," Faulk replied soberly. In the race between East and West, both powers were in the countdown. It was now or lose.

"I'm certain you do," the administrator agreed, "but it's more than that. Muff it and we might not get a second chance."

"Senator Halpern?"

Herndon nodded. "He's the focal point, but there's a whole host of malcontents . . . all screaming about the twenty-five billion that made this gamble possible. The stupid fools. Can't they see we're buying planets?" His face showed his annoyance.

"Cheaper than Alaska," Faulk said, "if you prorate it."

"You can't sell that line, Joe."

"What can you sell?"

"Success." Herndon leaned forward, tapping a stubby forefinger against the desk. "Reaching the moon and dying there isn't enough."

"I don't intend to die there," Faulk said calmly.

"You have to come back," Herndon insisted, as if he hadn't heard. "We need a Broadway parade, a tangible symbol people can see and hear. Remember the day John Glenn returned? Remember the national shot in the arm? They knew about it in Tibet, in Eskimo-land. That's what we need—a living, breathing symbol of success. Give us that and Halpern'll be screaming into a vacuum."

"I'll give you that, Phil."

"I know you will, Joe. I know you will." Herndon's eyes swept back and locked with his. "I envy you. I really do."

Karen was in the kitchen having coffee when Faulk reached home.

"Hi, honey." He tossed his hat on a chair and kissed her. "Kids asleep?"

"Kathy waited up till nine."

"Sorry I missed them." He hesitated. "I'll have plenty of time in the morning. I'm going in late."

Karen looked up. "Joe?" Her voice was very low.

He held her eyes. "I'm elected, honey."

She caught her breath, then forced a smile and said, "Ride that beast, boy."

"To the moon," he responded, immensely proud of her.

"Who's . . . ?" She didn't finish.

"I'm in the number one slot. I have Kovac and Mallon."

"Max . . . I'm glad for that."

"I'm glad for them both," he replied promptly. "Les is tops."

"Yes, of course."

"You sound doubtful."

"Not doubtful. I know Les is good."

"What then?"

"I feel sorry for him, that's all."

"Sorry . . . for Les?"

"He hasn't anyone," she explained. "He's going out of the world alone, Joe."

"I never thought of that."

"With no woman to wait for him, pray for him. Wouldn't you be lonely?"

"Of course," he answered, realizing suddenly how much strength he drew from her. Les wouldn't have that support.

"I love you," she said softly.

"I love you, too."

"We haven't much time, Joe."

"Plenty of time, honey, decades," he encouraged. "This will be a milk run."

"Milk run . . ." She tried a smile and he felt a wave of compassion. Sure, it'd be tougher on her. The women always took the brunt. He slipped his arms around her, gathering her in.

Chapter 2

X-day.

X-hour.

The steel gantry rolled back and Apollo, poised over 300 feet above the base of the great Saturn booster, pointed into the Florida sky. A light sprinkle of rain in the early predawn hours had broken; except for occasional white cloud islands, the sky was clear.

In a steel-reinforced concrete blockhouse over 800 feet away, the launch conductor, grim-eyed and weary, hunched over the master launch panel, facing a series of closed-circuit television screens. Bluish-gray tobacco smoke moved in small swirls toward the air vents. Figures wearing headsets sat along rows of instrumented consoles monitoring arrays of dials, gauges, meters, flashing green lights—oscilloscopes that displayed analogues of constantly shifting electrical patterns. The consoles were divided into two sets —one for controlling the ground support and vehicle systems, the other to measure performance. Occasionally someone stirred to adjust a setting or make a report; it was duly noted by the launch conductor. Favorable reports flowed in on the weather, surface and stratospheric winds, and from the range safety officer who manned the pair of destruct switches.

They had wrung out the rocket during the long hours of the night, step by step, each component, each subsystem and each system—electrical, electronic, hydraulic, pneumatic, mechanical. The huge tanking and pumping systems that fed cryogenic fuels to the various rocket stages had been checked; so had the gantry, the umbilical tower, the mass of machinery created to serve the bird on the pad. Finally they had checked the blockhouse itself— reporting systems, warning systems, backup equipment. Nothing had been left to chance. Now the launch conductor was undisputed master of the bird. To hold or fire—his was the decision. He felt unutterably lonely.

"Propulsion stage one?"

"Go."

"Propulsion stage two?"

"Go."

"Propulsion stage three?"

"Go."

"Autopilot and hydraulics?"

"Go."

Each question brought a simple answer. Reading from a prepared script, the launch conductor asked his questions with the precision of a metronome. Each answer was recorded. Around him batteries of automatic writers spilled out torrents of information, solenoids clicked, green lights flashed, machinery hummed. A brief hold occurred; a minor adjustment was made and the count resumed. Every face reflected the tension building through the night. Wind soundings were taken at 1,000-foot intervals between sea level and 50,000 feet. Wind direction and speed versus altitude were measured by radar. Flashed to the blockhouse, the results were duly noted.

A klaxon sounded, warning everyone from the pad.

At T minus two hours Joe Faulk had entered the lift in the umbilical tower, followed by Max Kovac and Les Mallon. Short and husky, Kovac's light gray space suit and equipment gave him a squarish appearance that reminded Faulk of a metal robot. The helmet concealed his coal-black hair but his deeply tanned face wore a quiet, serious expression. He entered the lift, nodding wordlessly. Mallon appeared almost gay in contrast. Medium height and wiry, with blond hair already beginning to recede, he nevertheless had an engaging lopsided smile and outgoing personality that made him extremely popular around the Cape. He was, as many learned, a practical joker.

He said carelessly, "Off to the stars. I always knew Les Mallon was destined to go a long way."

Faulk smiled dutifully, not quite certain of his own feelings. Elation, uncertainty, a curious foreboding held far back in the recesses of his mind—all were curiously intermixed. As the lift reached the top, he squeezed through the small hatch leading into the command module, casting a quick look around.

"Roomy," Mallon said cheerfully. "I could have brought a toothbrush."

Following a quick check of the life support equipment and instrumentation, they moved into the seats which, reclined during ascent, served as acceleration couches—Faulk into the pilot's seat and Kovac into the copilot's. Mallon occupied a narrow niche immediately behind them. Hermetically sealed, self-contained and self-sealing against leaks, Apollo's cabin formed a micro world. Oxygen supply, temperature, humidity and cabin pressure were automatically maintained; walls were constructed of thermal and acoustic insulation. Surveying it, Faulk recalled Mallon's description of it as "a hot-rod apartment" and smiled.

Settled, they plugged in the biomedical sensors to record brain wave, heartbeat, pulse and respiration. In space their reactions would be telemetered to earth, appearing as curves on graphs in Dr. Ashfield's medical section.

Now they waited.

Saturn swayed slightly in the breeze, a motion that Faulk sensed as disproportionately large. It gave him a sense of drifting. He heard the low whine of pipes as liquid oxygen at minus 297 degrees Fahrenheit flowed into the mainstage tanks, the louder whine as liquid oxygen and liquid hydrogen, the latter at a cold minus 423 degrees F., filled the fuel and oxidizer tanks of the second and third stages. The Apollo and Moon Bug burned hypergolics, room-temperature fuels which had been tanked before the astronauts' arrival.

T minus . . . T minus . . . The call, like a voice of doom, came over the phones. Waiting, Faulk wondered what the physiological data looked like now. The heartbeat would be moving up, the respiration increasing. He flexed his hands, imagining that he felt them tremble. The old jitters. They came before every flight. But this time, he knew, part of his emotion was founded on the possibility that they might not reach the moon. A thousand things could happen. They were slated to circle earth once or twice for final checkout. Should anything go wrong . . . Thought of being ordered into reentry brought a sickly grin. Nothing could go wrong, he told himself. The target moon was their pigeon—his pigeon. He'd wrap it up, deliver it with a pink ribbon.

T minus four minutes and counting.

The radio chattered:

"Telemetry to internal."

"Timer off-ready switch to ready."

Other voices broke in:

"Communications . . . go."

"Aeromed . . . go."

"Range . . . go."

T minus three minutes and counting.

At that moment the eyes of the world were on the great Saturn rocket, and on the tiny Apollo spacecraft crouched atop its nose. VIPs watched from a glassed-in area in the blockhouse. NASA officials, congressmen, scientists, military officers—they stared through the clear pane of glass, watching the countdown monitor, the TV screens, listening to the quick orders and replies. Five thousand people milled wall to wall in New York's Grand Central Station, eyes glued to the giant CBS-TV screen. Other millions clustered around televisions in schools, homes, restaurants, offices. Business had come to a virtual standstill. And where business moved, it moved to the cadence of the countdown. Drivers rolled their trucks with one ear glued to the radio. Saleswomen stirred restlessly behind tens of thousands of counters, waiting for the latest word.

High up at the edges of space, communication satellites intercepted, amplified and relayed launch preparations to the far corners of the earth. Italian, French, English, German, Japanese and Russian eyes centered on the rocket; so did Turkish and Chinese eyes. Children, grandmothers, peasants and merchants viewed with wonder the giant rocket poised under the blue Florida sky. Saturn had become an international affair.

T minus one minute and counting.

After that, things happened fast. Faulk felt the pressure—read it in the launch conductor's voice, the quick questions and answers that flowed over the radio. A mirror mounted over the viewport displayed the blockhouse and Cape—in this moment they appeared still and deserted. He would feel better, he thought, if Saturn were a piloted vehicle. Like the breed of men who flew the hot jets, he'd never accepted an electronic black box as the equal of the human brain. He'd had experiences with black boxes, knew all about malfunctions! Eying the red handle of the abort switch, he winced. Darned if he'd ever yank one again—not even with flames in the cabin. He felt the tension mount.

Motion picture cameras were turned on around the launch site. The stream of water shooting into the flame bucket beneath the mainstage engines grew to a torrent. At T minus 30 seconds the umbilical cables providing internal power to the rocket dropped away. The countdown went on. Faulk followed the stream of commands, the terse answers, strange noises that came from both pad and missile. Slowly he felt his own tension mount.

"Command module?" The voice jolted in Faulk's ear.

"Copilot?" he asked quietly.

"Go," Kovac responded.

"Engineer?"

"Go," Mallon sang out.

"Command module at go," Faulk reported.

"All systems at go," a voice crackled on the radio.

The launch conductor saw the green lights ripple across the command console as the automatic sequencer took over. Now the launch was out of human hands. Barring a last-second malfunction, the rest was automatic. The sequencer would do the work more precisely and more certainly than the coolest human operator. But the launch conductor could still cut the mainstage engines, a power he held until the last instant before lift-off. He swung his eyes to the image on the TV screen, his lips forming a silent prayer.

Five, four, three, two, one, zero . . . Ignition!

Mainstage!

A terrific din.

The stentorious bull-fiddle roar that swept out from the launching platform split the sky, blanketing and shaking the earth.

Saturn trembled.

Massive, ponderous, yet strangely graceful, it towered above the gushing flame line at its base, straining against the great metal holding arms that bound it to its pad while its spewing mainstage engines stabilized at maximum thrust. Faulk felt his own muscles strain with it. Muscles and nerves. From a lookout post beyond the blockhouse, Martin Lorry, the NBC reporter, anxiously gripped his microphone, exclaiming:

"Saturn's main engines are firing. Billowing steam from the flame bucket—a man-made waterfall under the mainstage to cool the fiery exhaust—blankets the lower half of the rocket. The Apollo command module holding our three astronauts appears like a tiny bug perched high on the nose. This is a day, folks, a day for history. Now, at any moment . . ."

Karen Faulk, clasping her children's hands, watched from the beach, unrecognized in the crowd. Unmindful of those jostling around her, she stared anxiously into the distance. All but lost in the billowing steam, the rocket looked a puny thing against the sky; but there was nothing puny about the sound rolling across the Cape. It came in crashing waves, reminiscent of the violent thunderstorms she had known as a girl in Wisconsin. She had liked it then, and the drumming, pelting rains that followed. But this was different. Her Joe was sitting in the very heart of the thunder. She felt the terror nibble at her heart.

"Mama?" Kathryn tugged at her hand. "Is that where Daddy is?"

"Yes, dear."

"Why, Mama?"

"Because . . . it's Daddy's job."

"Noisy, isn't it?"

"Yes, it's noisy." She looked down at George's face. He was three now. He'd need a daddy to raise him. Turning back toward the sound of the thunder, she forced a smile. "Ride that beast, honey," she whispered desperately.

Eve Kovac, tense and nervous, followed the launching on the television screen in her living room. She'd had some doubts about allowing David to watch. He was so young, and should something happen . . .

But David had come in as a matter of course and sat beside her, a dark, chunky replica of her husband. When the mainstage engines ignited sending up the billowing steam clouds, he said, "Seven and a half million pounds of thrust." She glanced proudly at him, marveling again at the precocity of a child of eight. "Wish I was there," David continued. "I'd sure like to see that old moon."

"Why, David?" The question spilled from her lips and she gripped his hand to still the sudden trepidation within her.

"Because it's there," he replied. "That's what Dad says."

When she glanced at him again, his eyes were on the screen, his face rapt with wonder.

A third watcher was Lily Jordan. She sat alone on a divan in her bachelor apartment, sipping a highball. As the rocket roared to life, she clenched the glass.

"Go it, Les," she murmured.

Lieutenant Colonel Joseph Faulk, USMC, faceplate closed and space suit inflated, felt the first quick vibrations as the five huge F-1 engines built up thrust. Over 30 feet in diameter and 130 feet high, the mainstage could lift six million pounds from the surface of the earth; with the stages above it, it could inject over 200,000 pounds into earth orbit. This particular rocket had been three years in building. Before that there had been long years of dreams, plans, blueprints, mockups, prototypes—incessant changes to meet each advance in the technology. It represented lengthy, bitter debate in Congress, hundreds of millions of dollars funneled to every part of the United States, around-the-clock work by small and large factories, shifts in local economies. It was also the product of tens of thousands of hours over drafting boards, in laboratories, at far-flung test bases. Now it stood ready for its few brief moments of life, to accomplish in that short span the thing for which it had been created—to thrust its third stage carrying Apollo and the Moon Bug to the near rim of the air ocean. It would do that job within a few moments of fire and fury; then it would die.

The sound spectrum rose to a tremendous rumble. Despite the padding in the reclined pilot's seat, the vibrations set Faulk's teeth on edge. He clamped his jaws to deaden the sensation. The dials on the batteries of instruments facing him danced—a wild, discordant dance; he blinked to bring his eyes into focus. The dials still danced.

All the way, he thought. *All the way. You're going to the moon,*

Joe Faulk. The flash of jubilation was swept away as a vision of his family formed in his mind. *Karen . . . she'd be worried as hell.* He was glad the kids were small. As the roar grew to a harsh bellow, the image receded. A tinny voice crackled in his earphones:

"Burke to command module . . ."

"Pilot," Faulk answered, happy to have Whitey monitoring them. But for a twist of fate, Burke could be sitting in his spot.

"All systems at go," Burke reported. "Looks good, Joe."

"Thanks, Whitey." He flashed a last look around. The cabin was small, slightly over 12 feet in diameter, with inwardly sloping walls. Into this small area were jammed the crew seats, now reclined at 45 degrees, the instrumentation and life support equipment. No square inch had been wasted: each had been accounted for. Soft sunlight, filtering through ports constructed of layers of leaded glass and plastics, splashed smoky rays across the console. Leaning back very still, Kovac stared ahead. Someone breathed heavily in the phones.

"Good hunting." Whatever else Burke might have said was lost as the metal arms holding the rocket to the pad were released. Faulk felt the first upward movement.

"Lift-off—the clock has started," he reported tersely.

"Roger."

"You're loud and clear, Whitey."

"You're looking good."

"Some shaking—not bad."

The first moment was the worst, not from the accelerative forces —they had not yet had time to build—but from uncertainty, trepidation, and with them a wonderment over why he was there. He had the sensation of uneasy motion, like riding a lifeboat on a comber-surfaced sea, the impression that Saturn hovered over the pad, fighting to get a finger-grip in the sky, desperately battling to keep from crashing back to the steel and concrete launching pad. The cabin seemed to sway, wobble, vibrate. Moving his head slightly, he glimpsed Kovac's helmeted profile. If he could see his swarthy face, it would hold a calm look, he thought. An Air Force major who'd flown everything with wings including the hotter than hot X-22 rocket plane, Kovac seldom displayed emotion.

The shaking became more violent. Through the ports he caught puffs of steam—against the clear Florida sky they appeared like gray-white mushrooms afloat in the blue. The sky was immense. The Cape, the beach, the throngs—Karen and the kids. When would he see them again? His eyes involuntarily riveted on the red switch that lay almost under his gloved fingers. The "chicken" switch. He winced. Not that he'd touch it, ever; but linked to a net of sensors that monitored every vital part of the rocket, it could work automatically—trigger powerful solid-propellant rockets that would hurl the space cabin to safety in thousandths of a second. Should a single sensor report trouble . . . He riveted his eyes upon it, sweating.

"Go, baby, go," the launch conductor prayed.

"Go, go, go . . ." A murmur filled the blockhouse, where all eyes followed the Saturn on the television screen. "Go, go . . ."

"Saturn's climbing, climbing vertically," NBC announcer Martin Lorry proclaimed in a too-loud voice. "It's a slow climb, deceptively slow, like a fly scaling the side of a skyscraper. The five giant F-1 engines are pouring out a savage torrent of flame—seven and a half million pounds of thrust. Saturn's commencing to pick up speed, clawing at the sky. Within a few seconds she'll begin pitching over . . . into a trajectory that'll take her into orbit on the first leg to the moon."

He paused, then forced himself into the grave voice his audience knew so well when he reported calamities and toppled governments: "This is an awesome moment, ladies and gentlemen. Here, today, on the fifth of July, 1969, we are witnessing the departure of the free world's first attempt to land men on the moon . . . an attempt which some scientists and politicians brand as foolhardy. But regardless of what happens, the names of . . ." Caught with his moment in history, he went on, speaking as if he had been in the innermost councils of the program since its inception.

Karen Faulk saw the rocket begin its slow rise.
"Take care of yourself, Joe," she whispered.

"Nice going." Burke's voice came through the phones, clear and calm. "You're going to turn a corner in the sky."

"Roger, I read you." Complex 39, from which Saturn was launched, was lined up with the downrange stations, but to get into a correct orbital path, it had to alter direction almost immediately. That's what Burke meant. An instant later the autopilot flashed a command; the engines gimbaled slightly and Saturn changed heading. Faulk felt the maneuver as a shift of forces on his body. The feeling of weight grew stronger, pinning him to the seat—an increasing pressure, as if loads were being heaped on his body.

"Going nicely . . ."

"Clear blue sky," he reported. "Fuel and oxygen steady. Cabin pressure 13.1 PSI and dropping."

"You're building up fast. How do you feel?"

"Fine." Faulk concentrated on the instrument panel. "The G's are still low."

"Max . . . Les?"

"Great," Kovac replied in an even voice.

"Like a butterfly in a hurricane," Mallon said.

"Mark one minute," Faulk cut in.

"Mark one minute. Roger."

The pressure mounted.

The roar came through the aft bulkhead like a vast thunder, strident, and the dance of numerals on the instrument panel became madder. Up, up. Faulk took a deep breath, sensing the growing acceleration. He sensed it as a growing weight pushing him against the seat, as a fear nibbling deep in the corridors of his mind. He had felt the fear on previous launchings during which they had practiced rendezvous with orbiting spacecraft. Having long since analyzed its nature, he realized it was not physical. Rather, it took the form of a nagging worry over the multitude of things which could happen to destroy or abort the mission. With it came an acute awareness of a slim margin of safety, and a realization of human frailty measured against the tempest in which he rode.

During the precise maneuver in which two spacecraft were brought together in orbit and coupled, the fear took another form— a sense of man's mental and physical limitations contrasted with the split seconds and errorless judgment required. In some three days he would perform those same operations in the bleak lunar skies. His thoughts were distracted by an intense vibration. High Q, the region of maximum dynamic pressure. He spoke abruptly into the phone:

"Entering max Q . . . a little rough."

"Roger."

"Sky is getting dark. Fuel and oxygen steady. Cabin pressure leveling off at 4.2 PSI . . . some sway and yaw."

"Read you."

"Roger and out." Faulk blinked his eyes at the instrument panel, trying to focus them. The numerals were blurred and wavery. This was the big try, the critical try. Dreams could unfold or crash. Whatever happened, it was his baby. Phil Herndon would be sweating it out. So, perhaps, would the aging Senator Ford Halpern, who'd opposed the program every inch of the way. A jillion eyes were watching him—friendly and hostile. They wouldn't say, *How's Apollo doing?* but *How's Faulk doing?* Let something go wrong and the reaction would be, *Faulk flubbed.* But he wouldn't flub. He kept his eyes on the escape panel, fearing the blinking red light that would spell the end of dreams. He knew the cold knot in his gut was related to the red light. No red showed.

"Looks real good." Burke's voice held a vibratory quality. Behind Faulk the huge thrust chambers, consuming the volatile mixture of kerosene and liquid oxygen, spewed forth high-pressure gases at more than 5,600 miles per hour. Four, five, six G— they were moving up fast. A red light blinked and he shot a worried look at the engine instruments. Number four was delivering slightly less thrust than the others. As he reported it, a mechanical device reacted somewhere in the complex of machinery; another mechanism shifted the fuel mix to bring it into balance. The red light cut off.

"Going, going . . ." The words echoed reassuringly in his ears. A hot metal ball burned in his chest and he breathed in short gasps at the top of his lungs, expelling the air against the positive counterpressure of the mask. His eyes burned. Dials with wavering needles, knobs with fuzzy numerals, a hellish mixture of noise, vibration, light—the world closed around him until nothing remained but the steel cocoon rushing through the purple-black void.

He clamped his jaws. They were being hurled toward a mysterious point X that represented a theoretical static spot in a universe filled with movement. He was riding a rocket sled, clipping the sage at Mach point 88, awaiting the fearsome moment when a plow beneath the sled dipped into a water trough, bringing the sudden deceleration that pooled body blood and dimmed vision. He was riding the sweeping arm of the Randolph Field centrifuge. He was . . .

"Ahhhh . . ." The gasp in his earphones jerked back his thoughts. Kovac? Mallon? *Himself?* The drumming in his ears brought vivid imagery of the fire storm spewing from the huge stern nozzles.

"Nice vapor trail," Burke announced, his voice reassuring.

The dense reaches of the troposphere—the weather belt where

storms are born—fell far behind as they hurtled through the rarefied stratosphere. At 21 miles a high-velocity jet stream drove west. Signals generated by a sensor flashed a message to a computer; quick calculations were made and an order dispatched to a mechanism controlling the engines. They gimbaled slightly. Saturn leaned into the blast, negating its force. As the jet stream fell behind, the engines gimbaled back.

"Pitch is 35 degrees. You look good," Burke said.

"Roger." Faulk spoke with effort.

"Going, going . . ." The G meter was fuzzy in Faulk's eyes. Seven . . . seven and a half? He wasn't uncertain. He saw only wavering numerals, an uncertain needle. A hand gripped his lungs, squeezing out the air. Lungs flattened, muscles taut, bones strained —his body felt distorted into odd shapes, twisted and stretched, buffeted by a thousand blows. Someone breathed spasmodically into the phones—a harsh, gasping breath as if marbles were rattling in his windpipe. Trying to turn his head toward Kovac, he felt a nauseating wave of vertigo. Each time had been the same, he thought—stinging eyes, hammering sounds assaulting the ears, face and body dripping sweat despite the cool air circulating in the suit, fears capped below the conscious mind. Did Kovac feel them? Did Mallon?

The voice in the phones crackled again, unexpectedly loud and clear: "MECO . . . on time." MECO—main engine cutoff. He felt it at the same instant, an abrupt lifting of the G forces, a stillness. "Staging . . ."

"Roger, I felt staging. We peaked at close to 8 G." The mainstage was a fist of power, a workhorse that lived and died in the thin shell of the earth's atmosphere. Separated from the rocket, the ring of engines would follow for a while before plunging back into deep parts of the air ocean, where heat generated by the friction of its swift passage would turn it to a blazing torch. "Escape tower jettisoned—light is green," Faulk added.

"Staging altitude 202,000 feet, range 52 miles, velocity 7,500 feet per second," Burke droned.

"Roger, reading you on Bermuda antenna now . . . much louder."

"What's your status?"

"Good. Cabin pressure holding at 4.2 PSI."

"Lovely ride," a voice exclaimed, as finished. It took him a second to recognize it as Mallon's.

"I'll echo that," he said. "Max?"

"Roger," Kovac replied, his voice as unruffled as if he were answering the phone in the house he rented at Cocoa Beach.

For seconds after staging the rocket glided through the soft dusk, seemingly without motion, for Faulk's eyes had no frame of reference. This was the stillness of space, an utter, deep, awesome stillness broken only by faint static sputterings in the phones. Like a cat creeping through a field of velvet grass, he thought.

Somewhere in the bowels of the rocket a programed command flashed to an automatic ignition system. Liquid oxygen and liquid hydrogen, forced through the lines by the pressure of helium gas, passed through heat exchangers, were vaporized and injected into the burn chambers. The powerful ring of J-2 engines caught, spewing a fiery exhaust as they developed thrust in excess of one million pounds.

"Burning," Faulk reported. "I see the booster . . . tumbling very slowly."

"Roger, understand." A harsh crackling filled the phones, rising to a banshee wail, dying and sputtering.

"Thermosphere." Kovac raised his voice, his eyes on the instruments. This was a region of rising temperatures, where atoms and molecules, bombarded by powerful electromagnetic waves from the sun, became ionized. Mingled with the waning and waxing howl came the voice from Cap. Com:

"Going, going . . ."

The second stage wasn't bad. Faulk felt pleased. It seemed impossible that the rocket could have weathered the hell of energies through which it had come without some malfunction. But that was just stage one. They still had stage two, stage three, the long trajectory—the moon landing. That, too, was just the beginning. There was the hostile environment, blast-off from the moon, the ticklish hour while the Moon Bug sought its mother ship in the black vault high above the lunar surface—the long hop home, and reentry. They had come but an inch of the long miles ahead, he thought. Here, in space, everything looked different than in the briefing rooms. Olson with his equations spilled over the blackboard, his voice dry:

"Here, at a speed of over 25,000 miles per hour . . ." He smiled grimly, thinking it indeed was different. Still, he took an intense satisfaction in relaying an "all green" report to Cap. Com. Phil Herndon would breathe easier. So would Karen, Eve Kovac, and perhaps a handful of girls with vested interests in Les Mallon. The roaring was closer this time but the sense of weight was less great, nor did he have the intolerable burning in his chest and sinuses. Dials had stopped dancing. The Christmas tree of vital instruments gleamed as a sea of green. He liked the color.

"It's a go bird," Burke said, his voice distorted by the seething ions. "Telemetry puts you on the button."

"Sweet words." Faulk felt the sudden lifting of the G forces again. "Second stage cutoff."

"SECO . . . we read you."

A slight jolt followed. "Staging . . ."

"On the button," Burke confirmed.

"I have the moon in the window."

"You'll have it in your lap in a few more days."

"Awaiting third burn," Faulk ended. With the soft thunder from the second stage gone, the rocket glided along its trajectory borne on inertial wings. The view was tremendous. Earth was a study in blues and whitish grays where cloud formations hid the sea. An island blocked up from the water. Twisting, he saw the continental land mass, the curving arm of Florida. They seemed far away. A sputtering cough came through the bulkheads, settling into a steady roar.

"Third burn," he said.

"Apollo?"

"Third burn."

"Roger, there's some noise," Burke declared.

"I read you loud and clear."

"Yeah, now it's clear."

"Instruments green and normal."

"You look good, Joe."

"This stage is a gravy train," he answered. He settled back, waiting, feeling his confidence soar. Third-stage acceleration began as the single, powerful J-2 engine flamed to life. Burning the tricky hydrogen/oxygen combination, it yielded far more thrust per pound than the fuel of stage one. It also was a more dangerous fuel —highly volatile, tricky to handle, still unpredictable despite constant testing. But it had the power. Converted into a gas and forced into the burn chamber, the resultant thrust came like the blow of a drop hammer. The noise was confined almost solely to the space cabin, for outside there no longer was sufficient air to convey even a whisper of sound. This was the aeropause, where atmospheric density and pressure equaled less than a millionth that at sea level —a darkening world where sun fingers vanished and the first faint stars glimmered. Stage three was designed to drive Apollo and the Moon Bug into parking orbit around the earth. Later, at a proper instant, the J-2 engine would fire again, driving them into the final moon trajectory. Then it, too, would be abandoned in space.

Despite the accelerative buildup, Faulk's body felt light—a curious lightness which he knew represented the stark contrast between the hammering thrust of stage one and the far lesser thrust of stage three. His instruments told him they were curving through the rim of the exosphere, a region of lonely isolated particles where molecular matter had almost ceased to exist. This was the very top of the air ocean, the realm first pioneered by Glenn, Carpenter. Russian astronauts. Sputnik had blazed its lonely orbit here. So had Mercury, Gemini, the early Saturns boosting unmanned spacecraft. Deep space probes had gone farther yet; many still sped their lonely paths, silent tombs of human artifacts, afloat in the vault of eternity.

The communicator gave a burp and a distorted voice came through. They were on course. Everything was fine. Stage three was performing exactly as it had been designed to function—giving the final push that would send them into a 100-nautical-mile parking orbit around the earth.

Faulk scrunched to one side, peering through the scope. Earth was a behemoth in space, a huge curved surface falling away in all directions—a plain edged with a curious blue where it met the skyline. It was far away. He shifted his eyes. Resting on the pad, even the rocket's upper stages had appeared gigantic, durable. Here, high above earth, Apollo appeared a fragile creature. He had the impression of brittle bits of metal, delicate shells enclosing even more delicate components; and the most delicate of all—the frail human shell which had the audacity to dare this thing called space. Apollo was a moth in a gossamer sky. He felt a sharp sense of insignificance—an ant trying to pilot a log through the cascades of a raging river.

"Stand by for third-stage burnout." Burke's voice tinkled, faint but clear, in the phones.

"Roger."

"Minus five seconds . . ." Faulk followed the sweeping hand on the clock. As it reached zero the huge J-2 engine sputtered and died. As the silent third stage with Apollo and the Moon Bug coasted into orbit, Kovac exclaimed fiercely:

"Made it!"

"On the button," Faulk affirmed.

"A fireball!" Mallon's voice held awe. "What'll I do for kicks after this?"

Chapter 3

Space is a vacuum, nothingness, yet not quite nothingness. It is infinity here and there occupied by microcosms called suns, huge groups of microcosms called galaxies, endless baskets of galaxies that form a universe. But the universe itself is but a speck in a limitless continuum, a shoreless sea circumscribed only by the limits of a mind which must measure to know; and finding space immeasurable, simply calls the unknown *infinity*. But this, too, is a relative term. Without top, bottom or sides, it goes endlessly on, encompassing in its midst an inorganic cycle of life and death and life again as its individual atom-stars burn furiously, die and are born anew.

Time and space are an entity. Both are without beginning or end. The birth and life and death of an entire universe is but a tick in the perpetual clock of eternity. Space is black, a deep, three-dimensional black in which such motes as the sun appear as rayless, brilliant spheres. Locally are a field of such spheres—huge bluish giants like Sirius, blazing yellows like Capella, reds like the baleful eye of Betelgeuse. Pure whites like Fomalhaut and greenish-whites like Castor and Mizar mix with stars of inconstant hue. In this local generation of stars, some are children; others are old—old as measured by the mind of man. Growing stars and dying stars form a small galactic community, unnoticed in the greater outer scale. Here and there are huge amorphous clouds—"dark nebulae"—island universes which in their drift through space blot out entire galaxies.

But space is rich in energy. It contains vast magnetic fields, radio waves, proton and electron storms, cosmic, ultraviolet and X-rays —messengers from afar. Some come from the furnace of the sun, others from deep places in the black where abide other suns; some cross the gulfs of intergalactic space. Here—and perhaps here and there—are minute bits of matter, incomprehensibly small, yet unique among all things in the space-time continuum, for they alone can contemplate on the nature of that which surrounds them.

They think!

They view the great vault above. They ponder shifting planets, eerie comets, the fixity of stars—at first with wonder, then with speculation, and finally, determination. They measure, weigh, calculate, analyze; and because of the inner nature of them . . .

They finally go.

Faulk unplugged the biomedical sensors, loosened his chest strap, unlocked the helmet visor and pushed it back. Next he disconnected the helmet hose, seat strap and helmet harnessing. Grinning smugly, he moved his hand upward. It felt effortless. He stirred—weightless, his body floated on a thin cushion of air. He was sitting, yet felt no pressure against the seat. His body felt as light as that of a mote drifting in a breeze, an eerie yet exhilarating sensation. Kovac had freed himself and was moving experimentally, testing his reaching and leg reflexes. Only Mallon appeared oblivious to weightlessness. Edging forward, he stared through the port.

"Good-bye, earth," he pronounced in an awestruck voice.

"Not yet, but soon," Kovac returned confidently. "An orbit or two and we're off." Faulk nodded, feeling the relief of having accomplished third-stage burnout. In a few hours, if everything was in perfect condition, the third-stage engine would roar to life, blast them through a space window into the final lunar trajectory. The "window" was a small, precise cube of space, like a doorway into another room. This doorway alone led to the moon; no other doorway would serve. Hitting it was a matter of precise altitude, attitude, velocity, time—factors which had to combine correctly at an exact spot in orbit to find the door.

While the others peered through the ports, Faulk reported to Cap. Com—speed 17,560 miles per hour, altitude 107 miles, on an easterly heading, a path he knew well. They were pointed toward Gibraltar in a course that would bring them down slightly north of the Canary Islands. Elation swept him. For a while he had held it back, scarcely daring to hope. Now it came like a tide, flooding body and mind. The moon. His was the first step. *Self-glory, Joe?* Ashfield's question popped into his mind. Yes, he acknowledged it. And pride. But there was also pride of race, the smug knowledge that man, after all, needn't be locked to the planet of his birth. The planets, the stars. There were galaxies out there, entire universes.

"You know, I have the definite feeling that we're going to see that moon," Kovac said, facing him. "It's never felt so near."

"The moon. . . ." Mallon's voice held a rare tinge of regret, for in the operational plan, only he would never touch its surface. He would remain in orbit with Apollo while Faulk and Kovac made the perilous descent in the tiny Moon Bug. Yet, as Faulk knew, Mallon's job could be the most difficult of all. He would be instrumental in guiding them to a safe landing—monitoring their return through the uncharted seas above the vacuum surface. And for a period of hours, possibly over a day, he would whirl in absolute solitude above the bleak moonscape, cut off from all his kind. He would be the loneliest man in all creation.

Sensing his thoughts, Faulk said feelingly, "You have a tough one, Les. We couldn't make it without you."

"Sure."

"You can be sure we couldn't," Kovac cut in. "This baby'll be our lifeline when we're squatting on the moon. You'll look like an angel up there."

"I'll keep out the doormat."

"And the porch light on," the copilot finished.

To conserve fuel, Faulk left Apollo in drift, a flight mode in which it used no power for attitude control. Faintly seen, the stars wheeled across the port, their direction varying as the spacecraft swung in pitch, roll and yaw. The earth rose and set, or moved laterally across their visual field. Faulk followed it, entranced. Vast, cloud-splotched, its horizon arched through space like a great bridge, the pale blue of its thin atmospheric band darkening with altitude. But the sky was black—a purple, velvet, three-dimensional black that spoke of incalculable distances; and in that purple-black he caught the glimmer of the firmament. Off to one side he saw the three-quarters moon; it hung in the sky like a pasteboard placard.

He let his thoughts drift. It seemed almost no time at all since the first Sputnik had whizzed through the heavens, less since John Glenn had pioneered the nation's first manned space trail along almost this identical orbit. (*He was flying jets then, thrilling to altitudes of 60,000 feet, crashing the sonic barrier.*) In memory, it was scarcely yesterday that the first of a series of instrumented probes had soft-landed on the moon to report conditions for the human who would follow. Even now three satellites circled the moon in uncertain orbits, placed there to serve as relay links in the Apollo-Moon Bug-earth communication network. He felt a deep sense of satisfaction. Apollo would carry the first humans to the moon. Apollo, under command of Joe Faulk. *From the Halls of Montezuma . . . to the cold, bleak lunar shores . . .* Humming happily, he caught Mallon's smirk.

"Already figuring how the Marines can grab the glory," he told Kovac. "Wouldn't that frost you?"

"We're outranked," the copilot answered. "Don't heckle him."

Approaching the first tracking station, Faulk corrected Apollo's attitude, then switched to automatic mode. A few seconds later the radio crackled:

"Apollo, this is Canary tracker. How do you read? Over."

"Like a bird," Faulk punned. "Loud, some noise. How me?"

"Loud and ditto. Please give short report on conditions."

"Cabin pressure 4.2 and stabilized," he answered. "Humidity 40 percent, carbon dioxide .03 percent and solar radiation normal."

"Roger, please send blood pressure."

"Will do." Faulk clicked a switch on the biomedical panel, beginning one of several such checks that would be made while in orbit. "Blood pressure start now," he announced.

The Canaries came up fast, dark, irregular daubs against the cloud-sprinkled blue of the Atlantic; they receded to starboard and within a few moments he passed into the clear and saw the northwest coast of Africa. Off to one side the Atlas Mountains fled past, a dark rope snaking toward the Mediterranean. Beyond lay a vast stretch of desert, pancake-flat and yellow-brown. His eyes flicked to the clock—four P.M. Greenwich mean time with the sun sliding into the west, yet scarcely twenty minutes had passed since their morning blast-off. With the sun an intolerably bright disk against the nigrescent sky, he dropped a pulldown filter shade.

Algeria raced by and almost immediately the deep space tracker in Kano, Nigeria, came on with a burst of static. Johnny Waco, a first-team astronaut posted overseas for the flight, came on:

"Kano on UHF/HF. How do you read me, Apollo?"

"Loud and clear. How me?"

"Clear, Joe. You're at T plus 23 minutes, 10 seconds," Waco reported. "You're on the trolley. Preliminary data looks good."

"I like those words, Johnny." Following the check-out, Waco asked: "How are your drones taking it?"

"Like seasoned space travelers," Kovac responded. "How's it with the earth mortals?"

"Envying you."

"Patience," Mallon counseled, "the second team will have its chance."

They chatted until Kano receded. The White Nile and Nairobi fled past, and far off to one side, the great towering fingers of Kilimanjaro. Crossing the east coast of Africa north of Madagascar, they sped across the Indian Ocean. The first sunset rolled toward them, a display of yellows, oranges, reds and purples, before they hurtled headlong into the cone of night.

Mallon gasped involuntarily as they watched in awed wonderment. Ten thousand stars blazed in the ebon sky. These were not the dim stars of earth, but suns—yellow, orange, blue and blue-white suns afloat like luminous ships on an immeasurable sea. Greens, scarlets, violets—they gleamed like the lanterns of a phantom galleon. Vast constellations blazed in undreamed splendor, hues that dazzled Faulk's eyes and evoked his imagination. He had seen the sight before, yet had never ceased to marvel.

"Magnificent," Kovac breathed. The radio sputtered, rising and falling, accompanied by a few garbled words. Faulk answered, sending out the call letters of a floating tracker he knew to be somewhere below them. He tried a number of times, finally giving up.

"Electrical storm," the copilot said. He jerked his thumb downward. Far below quick flashes of lightning pierced the clouds in zigzag patterns, blinding in their brightness. They appeared so near Faulk almost expected to hear the drumming crackle of thunder. The storm area receded and the clouds showed crisp and silvery in the moonlight. He continued to stare downward, caught by a sudden loneliness, puzzled until he realized why. Space, an immensity in which no human had ever ventured other than in brief orbits along the rim of the exosphere. Now, facing the real depths of the void, he sensed the complete isolation they would know. Karen, his friends, the world itself—everything would be reduced to a voice on a radio.

He lifted his eyes to the stars. *The human mind has been there,* he thought. It had touched upon planets and stars, had sent robots to the moon, to Mars and Venus, into great sun circles. It had explored galaxies heaped upon galaxies. Now unbridgeable space would be bridged. He would bridge it! Human life no longer would be isolated on a single planet. Man was on the march, following an age-long dream. Man, master of the universe—that was the essence of the dream. His course was outward. Looking at the stars now, they appeared closer.

"Should be crossing the Tropic of Capricorn . . . 90 degrees east longitude," Kovac commented. A moment or so later the radio crackled and the Muchea tracker on Australia's west coast came in, manned by a first-team astronaut named Gary Myers, less formally known as "Dad."

"How do you read me?" he asked, following the initial contact.

"Fine, Dad. How me?"

"Crystal clear."

"We passed over a lightning storm, missed the Indian Ocean tracker."

"They got your signal . . . radioed us. How's your status?"

"Good, a real green bird," Faulk replied.

"We have your speed at 17,560 . . . show an apogee of 176 miles," Myers reported.

"High enough for now, Dad."

"How's for a formal report . . . just for the record?" When Faulk finished giving it, Myers added, "Watch for Perth. They're lighting the city for you."

"Thanks, will do." As they made a time check at T plus 49 minutes, Kovac tapped his shoulder and gestured. Far below in the southeast Faulk saw what resembled a cluster of diamonds in the blackness. "See Perth now. Say thanks and hello, will you, Dad?"

"Will do." As Myers spoke again, Faulk caught the wistfulness in his voice. "Looks like you'll be getting a chunk of the moon. Wish I were with you. Go get it, fellows."

"Thanks. They should have made this an eleven-man crate."

"Next time. . . ." The static rose, taking on a high whine. A few moments later he talked briefly with Woomera and gave his reports, then switched Apollo to drift mode for the long span of the Pacific.

Hidden in night, Australia dropped behind and they raced over the island-laden South Pacific. New Caledonia, Suva, the Fijis, Samoa—they fled past unseen. Canton Island came in and an electromagnetic wave train passed between earth and the spacecraft, bleeding the latter of data. Fed into computers, the information was digested, analyzed and relayed to the NASA command post at Cape Canaveral, where final decision on blast-off to the moon would be made. Canton receded. The dawn line hurtled toward them. For a brief moment the earth was split between night and day, then magically night was whisked away. During this period they completed another item on the agenda—the vertigo test. With eyes closed, they moved their heads slowly up and down, from side to side, swaying back and forth while the Apollo swung in pitch, yaw and roll.

"Clear as a bell," Kovac reported, when finished.

"A floating sensation but no disorientation," Mallon decided.

"It's rather pleasant," Faulk agreed. He'd already pegged the floating sensation as due to weightlessness; shutting the eyes merely emphasized it. While Kovac made a thorough check of the life support equipment, Faulk stared ahead, watching for the first glimpse of the mainland. Finally the long finger of Baja California skimmed in from the east, its tip covered by huge thunderhead formations. Seemingly but seconds later the tracker at Guaymas, Mexico, reported their data "good."

Apollo cut the border east of El Paso on a course that would take them over Arkansas, Tennessee, North Carolina—out over

Cape Hatteras, into the blue Atlantic with Bermuda lying to one side. The curving arm of the southeastern coast lay in the distance. Clear and cloudless, Faulk thought it a beautiful day. Details of the topography showed with startling clarity—a ribbon of road, the Mississippi, the purplish Ozarks, clear-cut plats of farms.

"Can almost see the birds," Kovac commented.

Burke came in with a greeting from Cap. Com, saying, "Ninety-three minutes g.e.t. on one," which translated meant ninety-three minutes ground elapsed time since blast-off. "Orbital speed 17,560," he finished.

"Roger, how does it look?" Faulk asked, masking his impatience.

"What are your readings," Burke parried. Faulk gave them—fuel, environmental, power, radiation and biomedical data. "How about the impact counters?" Burke asked, when Faulk had finished.

"No tapping on the walls," Kovac cut in.

"Checks with the telemetry," Burke agreed.

"Now how does it look?" Faulk asked abruptly.

"Looks like you're it . . . on a data basis," Burke replied. "They're hashing over the go–no-go probabilities now, but I think everything points to go. Just a moment, here's Herndon with a message from our sponsor."

The radio sputtered as the administrator came on. "Congratulations," he began. "The decision—at this point—is go."

"Good," Faulk exclaimed.

"Here's the plan." The administrator spoke more briskly. "The present program looks good. Third-stage ignition will occur at T plus 169 minutes. It's now T plus 96 minutes, 20 seconds g.e.t."

"Check," Faulk replied instantly.

"If any change in readiness occurs, send an instant alert."

"Will do."

"We'll be in contact all the way. Good luck."

"Yes, sir, and thanks," he replied feelingly.

"Thanks to you . . . all three of you."

"At go. . . ." Kovac spoke wonderingly as the radio fell silent. He looked at Mallon and Faulk in turn. "Somehow I never really believed it."

"Neither did I," Mallon reflected. "Ain't it wonderful?"

"We've got a tiger by the tail," Faulk replied soberly, his mind on the long road ahead.

"We'll ride that tiger," he declared.

He gazed over the Atlantic, noting the gathering clouds. *Ride that beast, honey.* Karen's words echoed in his mind. Sure he'd ride it—to the moon and back.

The Canary Islands came up fast. Since their first passage the earth had rotated some twenty-one degrees eastward so that they passed south of the tracker. They split the west coast of Africa above Mauritania. The Sudanese Republic wheeled toward them and receded; clipping a corner of Ghana, they were hurtling through the Nigerian skies when the clouds closed in, giving Faulk the impression of a formless earth, dirty gray in color. The radio gave a few burps as Johnny Waco came on at Kano.

"You're at go," he said, following acknowledgment. "How do you read me?"

"Some noise."

"Same here. How are your readings?"

"Green and normal."

"Time check," Waco said crisply. "When I give the bird, it'll be exactly T plus 116 minutes."

"Roger." Faulk watched the clock. A moment of silence passed, followed by Waco's unmistakable signal. "Check."

Waco requested and received the instrument readings, then said: "You're a cinch, Joe."

"Blazing a path for you more sedentary citizens," Kovac interrupted.

"They'll probably be flying it commercially by the time they get around to me," Waco mourned. "I'll find myself hauling loads of lingerie."

"You'll make it sooner than you think," Faulk encouraged.

"Sure. Take care of yourselves."

With Kano fast receding, Faulk raised his voice: "Thanks, Johnny. We'll be seein' yuh."

"Next week," Waco replied, his voice spectral. "Make it good."

"Will do." The whine and crackle grew, then abruptly ceased; Apollo hurtled through the African skies in silence. Faulk eyed the clock. T plus 120 minutes—49 to go. Less than an hour, he thought. In less than an hour the big J-2 engine would flame to life, push Apollo to a speed in excess of 25,000 miles per hour— hurl it outward toward the distant moon which, in strange ways, had influenced man's destiny since the dawn of civilization.

They came out over Mozambique on the east coast of Africa, split the lizard-shaped island of Madagascar and met dusk and night in the Indian Ocean. They talked briefly with the floating tracker, and shortly after picked up Gary Myers at Muchea.

"T plus 143 minutes," he sang out. "Right on the button."

"Check," Faulk responded.

"How's for your readings, Joe?"

"Green and normal," he replied, conscious that this was it, finally and irrevocably. The long wait was nearly over.

Following a quick exchange of data, Myers said: "Cap. Com says go. Time to ignition"—he hesitated—"exactly 25 minutes."

"Check."

"Timer set?"

"Roger."

"Take it easy, fellows."

"Will do, Dad."

They chatted until Muchea grew faint and finally receded. Woomera fled by and a short time later Faulk saw the lights of a great city sparkling like a diadem far below and knew they were crossing Australia's east coast. The Hebrides, Phoenix and Canton islands whirled by in the night. Dawn came as a silver thread in the east, growing as it hurtled toward them. From time to time Faulk glanced at the clock. At T minus 5 minutes, he said quietly:

"Prepare for acceleration." Following regulation procedures, they fastened harnessing, closed faceplates and inflated their suits. Kovac switched on the biomedical sensors while Faulk trimmed Apollo's attitude.

At T minus 60 seconds, he spoke: "Engineer?"

"Go!" Mallon barked, his voice edged with anticipation.

"Copilot?"

Kovac said firmly, "Go."

"Apollo at go," Faulk confirmed, to no one in particular. His hands clammy, he felt a familiar tingling of the scalp, a sense of expectancy, a tautness of nerves poised for instant response. But this, he knew, reflected training, for there was no effective human response possible should anything go wrong. Leaning back, Kovac seemed shrunken into his seat despite the bulk of his garments. It was tougher on Max, Faulk reflected. He had few duties until they reached lunar orbit, when he assumed the task of navigation. His real job would begin when they entered the Moon Bug. And Mallon—his work would come in one huge bulge, starting with the Bug's separation.

His eyes fixed the timer. Minus 30 seconds, 25 seconds, 20 seconds. A low whine came from the oxygen and hydrogen fuel lines. At T minus 5 seconds he drew a deep breath. This, too, was habit. The first instant of firing came as a sputter, a peculiar cough that gave way to an uneven rumble, growing to a steady roar, which he sensed rather than heard.

"Ignition." He spoke quickly into the transmitter, his eyes

scanning the instrument console. A green board. A sense of pressure came, a growing weight, the fleeting impression of being hurled faster and faster. With it came the dull roar from the bulkhead, sputterings on the radio, a high whine he couldn't place. The job of the rugged third stage was to accelerate its upper stages from orbital speed to the speed of escape—over 25,000 miles per hour.

As the roaring continued, Faulk forced himself to relax, feeling the tensions drain from his body. The shifting forces impinging against him told him they were accelerating constantly, spiraling outward, moving toward the theoretical spot called the space window. Despite the fact there was nothing he could do, he kept his eyes on the instruments. Everything that happened now happened automatically. Man, just so much baggage, lay at the mercy of Apollo's brain. *A black box jammed with academic degrees*—that's how Johnny Waco had once characterized it.

The spacecraft's intelligence stemmed from a computer containing a miniature memory drum in which was stored the flight instructions. The computer itself was aligned to an inertial platform referenced to a particular point in space. The platform contained an accelerometer system which sensed speed increases in minute units, using these to send the computer the data it needed to issue flight commands. Rotating at over 6,000 revolutions per minute, it could handle 3,000 additions, 2,000 subtractions, or 300 divisions or multiplications per second. Using its 3,000-word memory, it commanded engine start, cutoff, staging, separation, and sent steering signals to the main engine and reaction control system, the latter controlling the small secondary jets used for attitude stabilization and minor velocity changes. Now, inexorably, the timer moved toward the second when a computer command would terminate third-stage firing. At that instant Apollo would be on its own, hurled outward by the forces of momentum generated by the J-2.

The radio sputtered and crackled, rising to a high whine. With the spectral noise came a voice from the Goldstone tracker, deep in the heart of the Mojave Desert. Apollo, Goldstone said, was on course. Time, speed, attitude, altitude—all had combined in a perfect match; Apollo was speeding toward its window. There were other words, savagely twisted by the seething currents of the ionosphere. Faulk kept his eyes on the timer. Minus 10 seconds, 9 seconds, 8 seconds . . . As the hand reached minus one second the computer flashed a command; abruptly the engine died.

In silence Apollo sped through space.

Chapter 4

NBC reporter Martin Lorry, conscious of both the TV cameras and his wilted collar, gave his well-known grave smile and announced:

"Ladies and gentlemen, the Apollo spacecraft is now on a moon trajectory. That is the word from Cap. Com, the NASA command post here at Cape Canaveral. Launching from orbit occurred over the Pacific scant moments ago." He gave a brief description of the event, adding: "Now I'd like to introduce Mr. Philip Herndon of the National Aeronautics and Space Administration, who has played a key role in the Apollo program. Mr. Herndon."

The camera moved, showing a stocky man with thinning gray hair, heavy shoulders and a face prematurely lined. He gazed speculatively into the lens. The scene faded into a long shot showing both men.

"How do you feel about the flight, Mr. Herndon?"

"Very good, of course. Everything is going like clockwork. We're extremely happy, and I might say, extremely optimistic."

"I take it you have full confidence in Apollo's performance?"

"Absolutely, and in the performance of the crew."

"I was about to say that. Have you been in contact with Apollo, Mr. Herndon? Since launch from orbit, that is."

"We are in constant contact."

"How do they feel?"

"Well, they've been pretty busy." Herndon smiled faintly.

"Of course. Have the astronauts any specific instructions?"

"I don't . . ."

"I'm referring to when they land."

"Yes, they'll explore, photograph the moon, return scientific specimens."

"Have you any expectations of finding anything startling, Mr. Herndon?"

"Startling? I'm not quite certain I follow you."

"Life forms, volcanic activity . . . I understand several scientists believe it possible."

"We're not anticipating it."

"Then you believe the moon is a dead world?"

"You could say that, yes."

"I understand there will be television pictures from the lunar surface. Is that correct?"

"That is part of our plan."

"NASA has done a magnificent job, Mr. Herndon."

"And the nation," he replied. "Apollo is a symbol of our scientific and industrial capacity, the determination and know-how of its people—the willingness to sacrifice."

"There's some controversy on that latter point, Mr. Herndon. Would you care to comment?"

"It's . . . a necessary sacrifice," he replied gravely.

"Would you explain that point?"

"We must go ahead or fall behind. There's no midway point," Herndon declared. "This is more than national prestige. It's . . . survival, as purely and simply as that."

"Are you speaking in a military sense?"

"Military, scientific, economic—they're one and the same. What I'm really talking about is a way of life, our culture. In another sense, this is part of our national development . . . as a people and as a civilization."

"I haven't heard it put in quite those terms before," Lorry admitted. "You feel, then, the moon is worth the billions we've spent to make this flight possible?"

"Definitely."

"I take it you have extreme confidence?"

"In the success of the mission? Yes."

"And in the ultimate value of the moon? I'm thinking of it as an investment."

"There are things on which you can't place a dollar-and-cent value." Herndon spoke in a chiding tone. "It's a necessary investment."

"As a matter of national policy?"

"You could say that, yes."

"Mr. Herndon, I understand this is a tremendously dangerous operation." Lorry leaned closer, cocking his head. "Could you say a few words about that aspect?"

"There is great danger," Herndon conceded, "but we've taken every possible precaution. Those men out there in space know their job—know it well."

"I have no doubt of that," the NBC man replied. "Could you name the most critical . . . the most dangerous part of the flight?"

Herndon looked into the camera, his eyes seemingly focused in the distance. "The unknown," he said quietly. "That's always the most dangerous part."

"Oh, give me a home, where the buffalo roam . . ." Les Mallon sang lustily, his face exhilarated.

"Spacesick," Kovac explained, winking at Faulk.

"Spacesick, my eye," Mallon denied. "Just happy to be here. I'm buying Phil Herndon a case of Scotch when I get back."

"A bourbon man," Faulk advised, momentarily discomfited. Les didn't know—would never know—that Herndon had allowed him to select his own crew.

"Okay, bourbon. Nothing but the best," Mallon promised.

"Nothing for the pilot and copilot?" Kovac asked aggrieved. "We're the ones delivering you."

"Just deliver me back, that's all I ask."

Faulk turned to the port, staring out at the sea of stars. Here and there were coal-black gulfs devoid of light, other places with star clusters so thick they appeared welded into a single blanket of milky radiance. This was space. Not orbital but deep space—the part of space called *cislunar,* which means this side of the moon. While hurtling in orbit they had been part of the earth, bound to it by strong gravitational tides. Apollo had been like a stone hurled at the end of a string. The power generated by the third-stage J-2 engine had the effect of cutting that string; now Apollo was being hurled outward, deep into the pit of night. He felt the stillness, broken only by the low hum of a fan that circulated cabin air.

With the first flush of excitement past, the enormity of the achievement caught him. Solemnly, almost humbly, he contemplated it. Far back on earth the computers had plotted their course. The complex machines had considered mass, thrust, velocity, time—dozens of variables. They fed on such data as starting point, gravity, earth rotation, perturbation of the gravitational field due to the earth's slightly unsymmetrical shape—had considered these same factors for the moon and the space-time relationship between the two bodies; from this they had drawn Apollo's trajectory. The path was a curved thread laid across a gulf, ending at a point where there was no moon, but where the moon would be when Apollo reached there.

Computers had charted the course, but man had built the computers, he reflected. Just as they had built the Saturn's stages, Apollo, the tiny Moon Bug designed to conquer a world. Incredible tools. Now, at the end, the final responsibility had been entrusted to him. The weight of command—now he knew how it felt. It hadn't seemed so great before the launch. Command, then, had meant glory, the limelight, public adulation. But here, in space, this fragile shell . . .

He let his eyes rove the cabin. Jammed with life support equipment, it looked incredibly small. Above him a regulator metered out pure oxygen, keeping cabin pressure at 4.2 pounds per square inch. Lithium hydroxide chemical sinks removed expired carbon dioxide from the atmosphere. Another unit balanced the heat gained from solar radiation against heat lost through conduction, maintaining the cabin at a comfortable 72 degrees. Magnesium perchlorate units removed excess water, keeping relative humidity within comfortable limits. Fuel and solar cells provided maintenance electricity; larger silver-zinc batteries supplied emergency power. He had lived with the design for so long that he knew every inch of wire, every cable, tube, instrument, plane and angle that made up the complex cabin structure—the double walls that provided protection against meteorite damage, the special double panes that filtered out harmful radiation, the complex biopacks that would sustain them on the moon.

His eyes wandered. Instruments were everywhere—detectors that measured galactic and solar protons, pocket dosimeters to detect the soft X-rays that preceded solar flares, gauges that recorded heartbeat, respiration, body and suit temperature. Space was divided between instruments that gave information and equipment that supported life and supplied energy. No inch was left unused.

Pulse counters to detect cabin or suit leakage, communication equipment that tied them with earth and later would tie Apollo with the Moon Bug during the perilous descent to and from the lunar surface—they rimmed him on all sides. But the god in space was oxygen. Tanked in spherical containers at minus 297 degrees Fahrenheit and shielded from the radiant solar heat, it constituted man's lifeline to the planets. Small portable tanks for later use were stored in the Moon Bug. Concentrated foods, plastic spheres of water, spare parts for critical components—he was contemplating them when the radio burped to life.

"Calling Apollo, calling Apollo . . ." Their trajectory and the earth's rotation had brought them into the cone of the Kano tracker and Johnny Waco's voice came through with startling clarity.

"Apollo. I read you loud and clear," Faulk answered.

"Preliminary data places you on the nose," Waco advised. "How does it feel to escape this trap?"

"Wonderful."

"The press and radio are going wild."

"They better wait till we make it," Faulk replied soberly.

"You'll make it. Wait'll you get back. There'll be a ticker tape parade that'll extend from San Diego to Boston," Waco told him. "You'll be as popular as Ronnie Silk."

"Imagine." Faulk grinned. Ronnie Silk was a youthful entertainer who had innovated a hip-swinging dance that was the craze of the teen-agers.

"We've got it all planned," Kovac cut in. "We'll make our dough giving testimonials for breakfast foods."

"I'll be your agent," Waco shot back. They exchanged data, then chatted for a while before he went off the air. Woomera came on later, followed by Canton Island, Goldstone and Cap. Com. Faulk chatted for a while with both Whitey Burke and Phil Herndon. After that came a period of silence.

T plus 5 hours. T plus 6 hours. Time, telescoped during the dangerous first phases, seemed slowing again, as if the hand of the clock were retarded. Once Faulk switched on his individual biomedical sensors and scanned the readings. Heartbeat 72, respiration 12, body temperature 98.4—his metabolic processes were slowing. At the moment the ride was as placid as a transcontinental hop in one of the big commercial jobs. More, for there was no vibration, no sense of motion, no wheeling cities, mountains or cloudbanks beneath—nothing but the vast plain of the earth and the remote, changeless stars. After a while he ceased looking and began inspecting his oxygen equipment.

Speeding along its trajectory, the Apollo spacecraft consisted of three major components—the now dead third stage, the Moon Bug, and the Apollo command module. These components had been coupled together in an exact manner to withstand the tremendous forces of pressure and heat imposed by the swift climb upward from the earth. Apollo's engine section was linked to a tough, hollow adapter tube, the other end of which was linked to the third stage. It was in this adapter tube that the Moon Bug crouched, a fragile moth in a steel cocoon. With Apollo and the third stage blocking the ends of the tube and the steel sheath encircling it, the fragile moon-landing craft had been protected from both the ripping winds of the atmosphere and chance meteorites at the edge of space.

Now, hurtling moonward at high-velocity escape speed, Faulk faced his first critical piloting task. The operational plan called for him to separate the Apollo command module from the Moon Bug and third stage and rotate it through 180 degrees around its longitudinal axis so that its burn chamber would point toward the lunar surface for retrothrust. Following this would come the most critical phase of the trajectory—bringing Apollo and the Moon Bug together. In this delicate docking maneuver, he had to couple the airlock on the space cabin's nose with a second lock on the Moon Bug, thus allowing them to transfer from one vehicle to the other. It was like removing a cigarette from a holder, reversing it and inserting the opposite end. Only this cigarette and holder were speeding through cislunar space at tremendous speed.

As time for the maneuver drew near, Faulk mentally rehearsed each step. He would actuate small explosive bolts to separate Apollo from the Bug, apply power from the small reaction control jets to move Apollo to a safe distance—use the same engines to rotate the space cabin so that its single giant engine pointed toward the moon. He had to control Apollo's attitude with minute precision, bring closure speed down to the order of inch/seconds. The time for electronic brains and automation was past, he reflected wryly. This was a piloting job, ticklish and dangerous. He was contemplating it when Kovac interrupted:

"Ten minutes to separation. We're in the cone of the Cap. Com tracker."

"Good," he exclaimed, relieved. The promise of activity relieved his tension. "Fasten seat belts . . . pressurize." He glanced quickly around. Mallon was buckling his harnessing. He caught Faulk's eyes and winked, then dropped his faceplate. Holding a gloved hand against it, he simulated a yawn.

"Might not be that boring," Faulk remarked.

"I'll sleep through it," Mallon promised.

Faulk grinned, taking it as a vote of confidence. Ready, he looked at Kovac. His face was hard, set, and his dark eyes held unspoken questions. They seemed to ask: *Can he do it? Can he control the small jets . . . the precise rates of closure?* Faulk closed his faceplate and turned a valve, feeling the cool oxygen balloon into his suit. It gave him a rigid, immobile feeling. He looked out the forward, side and overhead ports, calculating the view he would get during the maneuver. There would be times when the third stage and adapter tube holding the Moon Bug would be lost altogether—critical periods during closure when he would be unable to see the latching mechanisms. He must depend on instruments, his senses, the intuition built on long years of flying high-speed jets of all types. This would be like refueling in the blackened polar skies, only vastly more delicate and dangerous. He gave a last look around.

"Ready?" His voice came muffled in his ears.

"Roger," Kovac responded. As Kovac plugged in the biomedical sensors, the radio came to life.

"Ready for separation?" Burke asked.

"Roger, we are ready."

"Don't move Apollo too far from the Bug," he cautioned. "Keep your separation speed minimal."

"Will do."

"And use your exterior floodlights during closure."

"Roger." They discussed it briefly. Faulk was glad for the counsel. Burke had performed this same operation in earth orbit and he valued his advice.

"Don't hurry," Burke cautioned. "You have plenty of time."

"From here to the moon," Faulk assented.

"The brass wants you to stay on the radio—give a complete verbal description of everything that happens."

"In case we flub?" He grinned crookedly.

"To guide the next crew," Burke corrected. "It might be me."

"We'll do our best."

"Good, take it away."

"Thanks, Whitey. If we get in a bind, we'll scream for help."

"Your friendly earth adviser," Burke drawled. "We'll be standing by."

Faulk scanned the controls and instrument panel. Apollo's attitude in space was controlled by clusters of small gimbaling jets located around the periphery of the craft to allow it to be rotated in any plane. Each cluster consisted of one-, two-, five-, and fifty-pound thrusters which could be fired independently or in unison. Used together, they provided supplemental forward or reverse power. He had operated the system on simulators—long hours during which he knew he had mastered it completely. Now, in space, he felt a twinge of uncertainty.

With one minute to go, he unlocked the safety on the reaction control panel and flexed his fingers experimentally. The heavy pressurized gloves gave them a stiff, unresponsive feeling—too stiff, he fretted, for delicate operation of the firing keys. He shot a final glance at Kovac, who nodded. Behind the faceplate he appeared relaxed and calm, as if he had resolved whatever doubts he might have had. As the timer hand swept toward zero, Faulk unlocked and turned a switch that activated the separation system, saying, "Separation firing key on."

A scarcely perceptible jolt rippled through the cabin as small explosive bolts fired, freeing the metal band that locked the space cabin to the third-stage adapter. At the same instant he applied minimal thrust to the after jets, sensing a faint surge of acceleration. Apollo slid free of the metal tube and the gap between them widened.

"Range 20 yards, 30, 40 . . ." Kovac spoke into the transmitter, his eyes on the range radar. " . . . 50, 60 . . ." Faulk checked the firing angles of the forward thrusters and fired a short burst with the five-pound jets; Apollo began decelerating. " . . . 70, 80, 90," Kovac reported more slowly.

Faulk fired the thrusters again and a longer time ensued before the copilot called 100 yards, and finally 110. He trimmed their speed with the one-pound jets until they held steady at 118 yards.

"Steady at 118 yards," he reported. Remembering Burke's advice, he sat back and contemplated his position. The space cabin's nose pointed toward the moon, gleaming milky in the blackened heavens. Through the overhead and side ports he saw only the starfields—endless glowing lights. Below his feet was the earth.

Crouched in the steel cave of the third-stage adapter, the Moon Bug trailed behind, unseen except as a blip on the radar scope.

"Preparing for 180-degree pitchover," Faulk said, selecting the fore and aft one-pound thrusters to fire perpendicular to the longitudinal axis but in opposite directions, thus putting Apollo in an end-over-end spin. Conscious of the stiff gloves, he flexed his fingers and pressed the firing keys. "Beginning pitchover."

The instant the space cabin commenced rotating he sensed he had held the burst too long, yet hesitated to correct it. Next to oxygen, fuel ranked as the crown prince of space. Every ounce hoarded now meant that much more for the delicate moon maneuvers. The starfield swept slowly across the port and the rim of earth came into view, followed by the hulk of the third stage. The end of the adapter tube, pointed in his direction, seemed infinitely small.

"Overshot," Kovac said briefly.

He didn't reply. The earth filled the port, then passed from view, leaving only the starfield as Apollo hurtled through the night in a slow end-over-end tumble.

"Time our rotation," he instructed.

"Roger." When the earth's rim touched the edge of the port again, Kovac started a timer.

"Asleep, Les?" Faulk asked wickedly.

"Drowsy." Mallon chuckled. "Can't say that I've got my eyes closed."

Faulk spoke into the radio: "I'm letting her rotate a few times. Want to get the feel of it."

"Plenty of time," Burke encouraged. "Doc Ashfield's here . . . wants to know if the maneuver produces any vertigo."

"Not that I've noticed. How about it, Max?"

"None at all," Kovac replied positively.

"Les?"

"A pleasant sensation—makes me think of girls," Mallon answered.

"No vertigo, Whitey. Les has a few delusions."

"They don't count," Burke stated. "He had them before he left."

"Give Doc our best."

"Will do."

"Eighteen seconds," Kovac broke in, as the cycle was completed.

"Give me a beat count," Faulk ordered.

"Roger."

As the earth horizon swept into view, he pressed a timer button and began tolling off the seconds. As he reached ten, Faulk pressed the firing keys lightly. The earth came and passed again, this time in a rotational period of 25 seconds. On the next turn he brought the space cabin into alignment, trimming attitude until Apollo's nose pointed steadily toward the hollow third-stage adapter. The maneuver left them riding with backs toward the moon, looking into the vast sky-filling earth.

"Aligned for docking," he reported crisply. "Range, 120 yards."

"How's vision, Joe?"

"Eerie. The earth background gives off a creamy light, makes the third stage look like a blob—a curious shadowy effect."

"Can you see the end of the adapter?"

"A pinpoint."

"The doc is curious over whether you can judge distance."

"Not too well. We'll take the word of the radar."

"Don't forget your search beam."

"If we need it, Whitey. Don't want to blind myself."

"Roger."

"Beginning approach." Faulk fired a short burst from an aft-pointing thruster. Closing slowly with the third stage, he had no sensation of movement. Limned in the bright earthshine, the dead stage ahead formed a slowly moving splotch against the face of the planet. Kovac tolled off the range:

". . . 90, 80, 70 . . ." Nearing 40 yards, Faulk realized the third stage appeared as formless as ever and switched on the forward floodlight, reporting the action to Burke. The beam illuminated the interior of the adapter well, reflecting off the Moon Bug's glass ports. The third stage, a drifting derelict, presented a ghostly sight. Earth was magnificent—gigantic, sprawling, its mountains, seas and plains gave a variety of hues, here and there cut by great cloud segments. He fired a short burst from the forward-pointing five-pound jets.

". . . 20, 15," Kovac reported edgily. He fired another burst and after a moment the two spacecraft appeared holding a steady distance. "Closing . . . very slowly," the copilot finally announced.

Using the small trim jets, Faulk made minor attitude corrections, letting Apollo drift. After what seemed an interminable time, he felt that if he could reach out, he could touch the third stage. He made a final correction, aligning Apollo's airlock with the Bug's latching mechanism, visible inside the mouth of the tube.

"Final closure," he said abruptly. He touched the key of a one-pound jet, watching as the nose of the space cabin entered the end of the adapter. Switching off the search beam to conserve electric power, an instant later he felt a series of light bumps—"Like a ferry boat entering a slip," as Kovac described it. A flashing green light indicated that the locking mechanisms had engaged. Leaning back, he slowly expelled the air from his lungs, conscious that his hands were sweaty.

"Delicate," Kovac said.

"Doggone delicate. Check the airlock, Les."

"A two-room apartment," Mallon responded. "What'll we do with all the space?" Moving to the side of the lock, he opened an oxygen valve, checking the internal pressure by a gauge. "Steady at 4.2 PSI," he reported.

"Open 'er up," Faulk directed. Mallon opened the airlock, inspected the latching mechanisms, and finally unlocked the hatch leading to the Bug. Faulk followed him inside, switching on the lights.

"Mighty small," Mallon said ruefully. "About what you'd get at the Cape for two hundred clams a month."

Glancing around, Faulk saw what he meant. The Moon Bug appeared incredibly small and compact, far more so than it had back on earth. The side-by-side pilot and copilot seats faced batteries of instruments, controls and communication equipment—voice, telemetry, tracking and television that would link them with both earth and Apollo while on the moon. The bulkheads, deck and overhead were crammed with gear and equipment. In contrast to Apollo's powerful engine, the Moon Bug had twin descent engines that yielded a total of 13,000 pounds of thrust. Burning nitrogen tetroxide and UDMH, they were just big enough to do the job, and no more. A smaller set of engines provided go-up thrust. Symmetrical balanced tanks separately held fuel for go-down and go-up. Fuel for the reaction system was contained in a series of spherical tanks built around the vehicle's waist. In order to save weight during the critical launching from the moon, each item was jettisoned at the end of its usefulness.

Seeing it now, Faulk said humorously, "Still like to ride her down, Les?"

"Sure would, Joe. It's tough to come this far without touching the moon."

"I'll buy that, but you're going to have quite a job, Les."

"I'd still like to go down." Mallon cast a wistful look around. "I'll bet she's a real hot rod."

Chapter 5

T plus day one.

With the earth twenty-four hours behind, Apollo seemingly hung in space, absolutely motionless, as if pasted against the firmament. Seen from earth, the stars wheeled overhead, cutting great arcs in the sky. Here, except for Apollo's slow movements in roll, pitch and yaw, they were static, unchanging, steadily burning lights. Dominating the sky lay the gibbous earth; ahead lay the moon, grown and splendid.

If he could view it from a distance, Faulk mused, Apollo would resemble an artist's conception. He had seen scores of such drawings—silver ships against an ebon night, a backdrop of a million gleaming suns. They had appeared highly imaginative until now. He could look at such a picture for ten thousand years and it would never change. That's how Apollo looked now.

But there was motion.

He saw it in the dwindling size of earth, the growing size of the moon. Later they would reach a balance point where the two appeared identical save for their surface markings. After that the moon would explode with growth until it filled the sky. Grotesque, unearth mountains, awesome craters, flat dead plains called seas, and the curious rills which gave the moon the appearance of a cracked ball—these would become stark reality. He had seen photos transmitted by robot TV. Seldom clear, still they had disclosed a world of awesome contrasts, as if nature had designed it in a moment of rampage. Needle-sharp peaks, gaping fissures, solidified lava rivers—these were the outlines of the vagabond world upon which they would land. Their particular destination was *Oceanus Procellarum,* the Ocean of Storms, a huge sweep of plain lying in the moon's western hemisphere. It had been selected as the flattest spot suitable for their purpose.

Contemplating it, he prepared for the next phase of the operational plan—jettisoning the dead third stage and adapter. The structure had been retained following engine cutoff to serve as a shield during passage through the dense meteoroid belt around earth, and later to stabilize the unmanned Moon Bug during separation, pitchover and remate. Now the impact counters indicated meteoroid danger as negligible. The hazard would increase as they approached the lunar surface, but by then the Moon Bug had to be free. Early jettisoning would allow them to extend the Bug's antennas and radar dishes, thus testing its communications. Kovac was discussing it with the Cape.

"I'd dump it now," Burke advised. "You'll want to be well clear of it when you apply retrothrust."

"That's how Joe figures."

"Things pretty comfortable up there?"

"Boring." The copilot affected a yawn. "Why?"

"From your biomedical data, we'd guess you were hibernating."

"Les does the sleeping. Joe and I attend shop."

"Conserving my energy to rescue these goons when they're lost in space," Mallon cut in.

"Dreaming of girls," Kovac corrected. "It's all he does."

"Girls?" he asked innocently.

"You should know," Burke drawled. "We had an anxious call from one this morning—the private line. Wonder how she got the number?"

"One of the many," Mallon murmured. "What was her name?"

"Lily Jordan. She sounds like quite a dish."

"I seem to recall," he reflected. "You know how it is with a popular bachelor."

"I've got her number," Burke said smoothly.

"You've what?" he asked aghast.

"So we can keep her informed. You wouldn't want the poor girl to worry."

"Personal therapy—I can see it now," Mallon moaned.

"We're keeping Karen and Eve advised," Burke continued. "They're taking it in great stride."

"Thanks," Faulk said simply.

"The kids are fine."

"Worried?"

"Not a bit. You know kids. They think it's a great adventure— something straight out of science fiction."

"Isn't it?" Kovac asked.

"Not any more, Max." They talked until Faulk was ready to jettison the third stage and adapter. Tumbling slowly in drift mode, the third stage was eclipsing the moon. He stabilized the rocket with the small jets, then rotated it in pitch until the third stage pointed toward earth.

"Ready for jettison," he reported. As Burke rogered, he actuated the separation system, sensing a slight jolt as the dead booster section and tankage broke free. Seconds later he dumped the steel adapter housing the Moon Bug, then applied thrust from the attitude-control engines. Clear of the debris, he fired retrothrust, trimming final velocity with the small one-pound jets. Finished, he rotated Apollo in pitch, bringing its burn chamber pointing toward the moon. The adapter and third stage trailed far behind, tumbling blackish blobs against the earth's creamy face.

Unmasked from its steel shell, the Moon Bug cut an ungainly figure. Misshapen, incredibly small, four stubby legs protruded from its pear-shaped body. Extended during landing, they were backed by layers of crushable foam designed to absorb the impact energy during landing and protect the engine and space cabin from damage. Small ports gave a view to the side and overhead; a bulged, downward-looking window gave the pilot a view of one of the touchdown pads. Riding with their backs toward the moon, they stared squarely into it, giving Faulk the impression of riding the center car of a subway train.

Seeing the Bug now, stripped of its cocoon, he thought it weird, and wonderful. It resembled a vehicle from fantasy-land. Sunshine reflected off its planes and contours cast it in light and shadow. Clearly this was a vehicle for space, for its weird angles defied every known law of aerodynamics. It was a ship designed for a vacuum.

"Like a giant crab," Kovac observed.

"Or a lopsided igloo with legs," Mallon supplied. "How do you suppose they ever arrived at that design?"

"What do you want—a Cadillac?"

"Would be nice," he agreed.

"I'll settle for it," Faulk declared.

He had lived with the Moon Bug for several years and knew it intimately, inside and out. Selected as the best of many designs, it represented the peak of American technology and industry. He had studied it as a blueprint, seen it slowly take shape in the factory—had watched it tested in a score of ways. He was satisfied it would take them from lunar orbit to the surface and back. It had been designed for that one specific purpose, and no more. The air ocean that surrounds earth demands symmetry—an alien word on the moon, where nothing is symmetrical. No external forces existed to retard the Bug, or buoy it. No winds blew in the lunar skies, no rains fell, nor were there clouds. A distorted world, it had never known the soothing forces of gradation. Garish rocks, fantastic cones, blazing, intolerable two-week-long days and equally long nights when temperatures dropped to minus 250 degrees Fahrenheit—those were the ingredients of the hostile environment toward which they sped. "A world of unlife," Herndon had called it. Alien, deadly and bizarre, but a planet to be won, he mused. The inevitability struck him like a force.

According to computations, Apollo would intersect the moon's orbital plane in slightly under T plus 72 hours, a time still over 40 hours away. With the novelty of space wearing thin, they kept busy to offset the boredom. Using Mallon's seat which made down into a pad, they took turns sleeping. Eating, caring for their bodily needs and checking equipment quickly became routine. Faulk and Kovac occasionally talked with Burke, Waco and Myers, or the people who spelled them off, for NASA's deep space-tracking facilities around the globe provided a constant link. Routinely, too, they checked and reported readings from the myriad of instruments—radiation counters, erosion counters, life support and power indicators—dials and gauges that told how they were faring in the vast sea between earth and its milky-faced daughter.

Ashfield was interested in their daily routine. *How bored are you? How does it affect you? Are you jittery . . . nervous? Do you have vague fears?*

"My only complaint is the lousy chow," Mallon told him. "Who made it—a chemist?"

"Yes," Ashfield answered gravely.

Despite the monotony of the long coast period, Faulk had difficulty relaxing. Death in space was a many-faceted thing. It could come in the form of a solar flare, a meteor, or some vital piece of equipment that refused to function. It was, as Herndon had warned, "like an unwanted guest—always at the door." Apparently Kovac felt the same for, as Faulk noticed, he spent an inordinate amount of time checking the various readings. Only Mallon seemed unaffected; he could nap at the slightest opportunity.

Pulled by the tug of earth, Apollo was decelerating. It would continue to decrease speed as it moved outward. By the time it reached the neutral zone where the gravispheres of earth and moon canceled each other—a scant few thousand miles above the lunar surface—it would be traveling at ebb speed. Then, caught by the moon, it would accelerate faster and faster until braked by the retrothrust of Apollo's main engine. That hour occupied Faulk's mind.

He attempted to anticipate every contingency. Fuel was at a premium, both in Apollo and the Moon Bug. It had been calculated and doled out on earth, almost to the last pint; none was left for excessive maneuvering, none to correct mistakes. Each engine firing, whether of Apollo or the Bug, had to perform a given task— accelerate, decelerate, or shift the vehicle's attitude or flight path. He formulated the plan in his mind. At a precise point determined by the computers, he would fire main engine retrothrust. Approaching the moon on an elliptical path, Apollo would correct into an equatorial orbit a scant hundred nautical miles above the airless surface. While circling the moon they'd correct their maps, note landmarks, check Apollo's exact orbit time—prepare to descend.

He reviewed each step, each operation, each fleeting second that lay ahead. Deceleration, altitude, attitude, mass—these and a dozen other variables would summate in a single critical moment; balancing them would be the X in the equation.

He was the X.

T plus day two.

"It's a sweet bird," Kovac said.

"Sweet," Faulk reverently agreed, fingering the controls.

Seated in the Moon Bug, they were testing and rehearsing the procedure they would follow after separation from Apollo. The side-by-side seating gave each man full access to all controls and instrumentation, thus allowing Kovac to serve as backup in case of emergency. As copilot, he navigated, monitored the instrument console and aided with communications—in short, was Faulk's eyes and ears.

Finished testing the communication systems—voice, telemetry, radar and television links that would tie them with Apollo and earth —Faulk turned his attention to the ports. There he felt unhappy. Lateral and overhead vision were good but the engine location blocked his view underfoot. Only by scrunching his body awkwardly and peering through an offset pane could he see one of the touchdown pads. It was little enough to go on.

"We'll have to depend mainly on radar altimeter, scope and closure rate," Kovac ventured. "Float down like a feather."

"A feather." He grunted.

"We can hover at low altitude—check the surface for dust and hardness," the copilot pursued.

"I'm worried about that."

"Dust?"

"Obscuring the landing," he explained. "The exhaust could kick up a real blizzard."

They considered it silently. This wasn't a new problem. It had been anticipated and debated since the first unmanned probes had shown the lunar surface to vary from barren rock to areas covered with a fine ash that ranged from a few millimeters to many yards in depth. Landing in the latter would be disastrous.

"We'll have to tough it out," Kovac finally suggested.

They discussed it. NASA had decided on a night landing on the basis that the lunar cold could be combated more readily than the blazing daylight heat. Faulk agreed, but with reservations. The tentative landing site, illuminated by earthshine, lay a few degrees inside the sunset line. At earth noon on a sunny day in the middle latitudes, light from the sun would approximate 10,000 footcandles. In the lunar night, lit only by earthshine, it would be two footcandles at most, and probably but a fraction of that. What would a jagged peak look like in such light? A chasm? He didn't savor the prospect.

"Ash storms plus night—could be a real picnic," he observed cynically.

"The search beams will help."

"Will they, Max, in a dust storm?"

"We can hover," the copilot persisted.

"Not long. Once we start down we're burning fuel."

"We'll make it." Kovac's eyes crinkled humorously. "We won't know till we try."

"We sure won't."

"It might prove a cinch."

"An optimist," Faulk declared. "Well, we'll give it a pitch."

"I can see us now, riding down Broadway."

"Broadway—that's a world away."

"A joker," Kovac cracked. They returned to the main cabin, where Mallon was lolling in the pilot's seat.

"Thought you'd got lost," he drawled. "I was just about to go on alone."

"Without the navigator?" Kovac asked. "You'd never get there."

"How could you miss?" Twisting, he looked through the port. Vastly larger, the moon filled the sky. Its mountains and dead seas had taken on a new form—that of a stark painting done in blacks and whites. Its lines were bold and grim. In contrast, earth had shrunk. It hung in the sky as a great quarter crescent, its lighted areas startling clear in greens, blues and browns. Faulk searched the sky. The third stage and adapter had vanished from sight. The radar showed them at a distance of nearly 30 miles on a somewhat divergent course, which he attributed to the slight forces exerted on the jettisoned sections during separation.

"Perpetual orbit," Kovac remarked, viewing them on the scope.

"Someday, perhaps, space travelers will run across them . . . and will wonder," Faulk replied musingly.

"Probably haul them off to the Smithsonian Institution," Mallon jibed. "We should have chalked our names on them."

"Don't worry, Les." Faulk faced him. "Your name's secure in history."

"If we don't crack up this bucket of bolts."

"A distinct possibility." He looked at the food cabinet. "Time for dehydrated concentrates of something or other."

"I'd rather not know what," Mallon said. "I honestly wouldn't."

Two things happened that day that shook Faulk. A flashing red light on the instrument panel indicated a malfunction in the small fan that circulated cabin air. Mallon quickly found and repaired it. It wasn't much, but it served to remind Faulk that even the most reliable components were subject to failure. Shortly after, a raucous horn blared accompanied by another red light.

"Meteor impact," Faulk barked. He flipped his faceplate shut and pressurized his suit with a single motion. A glance told him that Kovac and Mallon had reacted automatically, even though the latter had been napping when the alarm sounded. He swung his eyes to the pressure gauge. Four point two PSI—the needle clung there.

As the pressure remained unchanged, Kovac conjectured: "Either a small particle that didn't penetrate or the wall has resealed."

"Probably." Faulk studied the impact counter.

Mallon declared fervently, "Let's hope it's a random strike. I'd sure hate to wind up in a shooting gallery."

"You'd make a lovely clay pigeon," the copilot affirmed.

"A hero never has feet of clay."

"We can't count on it being random," Faulk cut in. "We're not certain of the meteoroid density around the moon and we're getting close."

"If they have to hit, let's hope they're small," Mallon observed.

Faulk looked at the others, saying reluctantly, "From here on out, one of us will have to stay under pressure at all times." Kovac grimaced. At best, living in a pressurized suit was bad.

"I'll volunteer." Mallon grinned. "I'll sleep with my faceplate closed."

"Accepted," the copilot said quickly.

"We'll spell one another off in short takes," Faulk decided. He reported the occurrence to Cap. Com, then settled back, his eyes on the timer.

Day three was going great.

The moon filled the sky, a monstrous sphere of distorted rock hurtling through the eternal silence of space at some 2,300 miles per hour. Rotating on its axis in a little more than 27 days, its mass was but slightly over one-eightieth, its volume one-fiftieth and its gravity one-sixth that of the parent planet, which had receded to a sphere slightly larger than four times that of the moon as seen from earth. It moved along its elliptical path in majestic grandeur, alternately approaching to within 222,000 miles of earth, retreating to over 252,000 miles.

Now a three-quarter moon, its darkened quarter gleamed visibly in the earthshine. The Alps, Apennines, Leibnitz and Doerful ranges lay stark and oddly patterned, their black shadows revealing heights and grotesque malformations. New craters had sprung into view—thousands of them. Copernicus rising from a dead sea, Tycho in the lunar uplands, the scooped-out appearance of Grimaldi— they took on new form. Mare Imbrium, a great elliptical plain bounded on three sides by mountains, opened in the west into Oceanus Procellarum, the Ocean of Storms. Faulk studied the latter intently. Down there some place, just across the sunset line, he would set the Moon Bug down. His eyes sought details. Long narrow rills slashed across its surface in irregular geometry, and light-colored streaks radiated outward from several craters.

"Mountains," Mallon remarked, following his eyes.

"Riphaen hills," Kovac said authoritatively. "Small and well out of the landing area."

"The surface doesn't look smooth," Faulk observed, as if he hadn't heard. "I get the impression that it's rolling, even the central area."

Kovac studied it through the scope. "Could be right," he said finally. "There's an undulating pattern, at least in parts."

"We'll know better when we're in orbit."

"Yes, we'll know better." Their eyes met briefly.

As the day drew to a close, the radio crackled. Burke was back again. After a brief conversation he said, "You're closing fast. Let's have a time hack to retrothrust."

"Standing by," Faulk acknowledged.

"T minus 2 hours and"—a long pause followed—"10 minutes exactly."

"Check, 2 hours 10 minutes to retrothrust." Kovac gave the readings, then Faulk and Burke talked over some of the problems that might be encountered following engine firing.

When they were through, Burke said, "Now, Joe, we have someone with a message for you." Before he could grasp Burke's meaning, another voice came through the phones:

"Joe . . ."

Karen! Elated, he leaned forward as if to cup his voice, exclaiming, "Honey, it's good to hear from you. How are you?"

"Fine, wonderful. The children are fine." The words spilled over the phones as if she were trying to say everything at once. Catching herself, she slowed down. "We're all right, Joe. It's you we're worried about. How are you?"

"Fine."

"The children keep asking about you," she said in a low voice.

"Tell them not to worry, honey. Daddy will be home soon. Give them my love."

"I do, Joe, every night—" She broke off, then added, "Everyone has been grand."

"It won't be long, honey," he encouraged.

"It's been years."

"Three days. Only three days."

"Take care of yourself, Joe. Hurry home."

"As fast as this crate will bring us," he promised.

They talked a few moments longer, then murmured good-bye. Turning, he saw Kovac's expectant face; an instant later Burke broke in:

"Max . . ."

"Here," the copilot said, trying to control his eagerness.

"Max, Max dear . . ." Eve's voice came softly. "Are you safe?"

"Safe as I'll ever be. Don't worry."

"That's a foolish admonition." Her voice rose. "David's so excited. He's a real hero at school. Last night his picture was in the paper."

"Tell him I'm fine," he encouraged.

"I will, Max, I will."

As they talked, Faulk cast a glance at Mallon. His face had taken on a dejected cast and Faulk felt a sweep of sympathy. As Karen had said, there was no one to bid him good-bye or to pray for him, no one waiting. The lonely life. He hoped that Burke . . . As the thought ran through his mind, Kovac finished and Burke cut in:

"Les?"

"Me?" Mallon exclaimed, surprised.

"Anyone else there by that name?" Burke asked.

"I'll accept the call," Mallon declared grandly.

"*Les, boy . . .*"

"Lily," he answered in a pleased voice. "How are you, baby?"

"Fine, Les. Wasn't it nice of Mr. Burke to invite me?"

"Nice guy," he replied offhandedly.

"How are you, Les? What are you doing right now?"

"Just barreling along at umpteen thousand miles per hour," he drawled nonchalantly, holding his gloved hand as if studying his fingernails. "Heading for the old rock pile."

"Take care of yourself, Les."

"Don't worry. Say, honey, how'd you like to ride in a parade?"

"Parade?"

"Down Pennsylvania Avenue . . . when we get back," he explained. "Of course there'll be company. We'll have to invite Joe and Max. They're helping me, you know."

"You're a lovable fool, Les Mallon," she replied softly. "Just come back."

"We'll be headed for the barn before you know it," he promised. "I'll bring you some moon dust. Very romantic."

Faulk and Kovac chuckled. When the conversation finished, Burke cut in: "Stand by, Joe. We're expecting someone else . . . any minute now."

"Herndon?"

"His boss. Oh, here we are." Burke's voice grew suddenly subdued, just as suddenly growing formal: "Captain Faulk?" His tone brought the pilot's head up sharply.

"Never mind the introductions," another voice cut in quietly. "I feel as if I know Joe Faulk personally, and Max Kovac and Les Mallon too." A soft chuckle came and he added, "They're certainly getting the publicity."

Faulk shot a startled glance at the others as the voice went on, speaking more formally this time: "Personally, and in behalf of the people of the United States, I want to convey my sincere wishes for the successful completion of your mission." That voice, Faulk thought, awed—he would know it anywhere. Any American would.

"The nation is following your flight with admiration. We wish you Godspeed." A few more words followed in the same vein before he finished.

"Thank you, Mr. President," the three exclaimed almost simultaneously.

The soft chuckle came over the wire again, and after a brief silence, Burke spoke: "T minus one hundred eleven minutes . . . exactly. We'll be standing by."

"Thanks, Whitey," Faulk answered. "You've made this quite a day."

"A better day when you return, Joe." His voice rose. "Take it away. . . ."

Chapter 6

The moon hurtled toward them, pocked, distorted, a violent scape in blacks and whites. Serpentine mountains crawled over its surfaces and its never-never seas lay flat and gridded, here and there broken by great cleavages. Awesome cones rose abruptly in splendid isolation, at the distance visible as dark rosettes. Their long shadows cut black notches in the dead sea bottoms. Other cones appeared in clusters and chains, as if mass-produced of bubbling rock in the dawn when the moon was new.

Faulk watched, fascinated by the unfolding tableau. Lying at a sharp angle to the sun-earth line, three-fourths of its bleak surface, washed in the solar rays, was limned in stark detail. The Terminator, the line separating night from day, cut a sawtooth across mountains and plains, leaving the other quarter splotched and leprous in the earthshine. This latter was the *ghost moon,* a world of half-light in which cones and mountains showed as dark splotches against a cream-dusk background. It was, he thought, a tangled geometry without rhyme or reason, a world fashioned without plan. Without softness, pleasant slopes or rounded hills, yet it gripped his imagination. Here was nature in the raw—stark, wild, untamed. No leavening hand had ever caressed that rugged scape, no breeze or gentle rain. This, he reflected, was a world unchanged in the march of eons.

He shifted his eyes to the countdown timer. *T minus 9 minutes.* Waiting, he felt the tension build, and with it a sudden acute loneliness. Burke, Waco, Myers, all of the resources of NASA were as close as his mike; their knowledge and skills were his for the asking. He had Kovac to back him, and Mallon. Yet, with all that, the feeling of being cut off from all his kind persisted. The weight of command, he mused—the loneliness of a general at the head of his army as he awaited battle. This was his hour, his responsibility—his command. How would Les feel when, alone, he rode Apollo through the skies of this alien realm? I'm lucky, he thought, at least I'll have Max. Les will have no one at all. Now and then there would be a voice on the radio, but mainly only silence. What did Les think? Aside from a bit of clowning, he had never voiced his thoughts on the subject. Did he welcome it? Dread it? He didn't know.

The timer hand moved on. At T minus 6 minutes he issued a brief order. Closing his faceplate and inflating his suit, he spoke into the radio: "Apollo calling Cap. Com. . . ." He repeated the call several times.

"Roger, we read you." The voice, faint but clear, unmistakably was Burke's.

"Beginning attitude correction preparatory to retrothrust," he reported.

"Roger, keep in touch."

"Will do."

Glancing at Kovac to check his readiness, he scanned the attitude controls, flexing his fingers to assess their sensitivity. With the firing sequence in mind, he unlocked the firing keys and fingered them lightly. A single one-pound jet atop the main engine housing gimbaled, fired, and almost as quickly cut off. It was a small thrust, scarcely measurable against the mass of the body, yet sufficient to tilt the craft on its longitudinal axis; the engine section began swinging downward in a slow arc. The stars swept slowly across the ports. Scant seconds later he gimbaled another engine and fired it, countering the motion. Kovac, studying the lunar horizon indicator, switched his eyes to a visual scope, then consulted some data readouts.

"On the button," he announced finally.

Satisfied, Faulk fired other light thrusters—jets that rotated the spacecraft slightly on its long axis, others that altered axial direction in the lateral plane. Conscious of the scant amount of fuel, he took his time, mentally rehearsing each operation before he made it. Later, in the Moon Bug, there would be no time for rehearsal—no extra seconds could be bought; but now, while he had time, he used it fully.

Kovac monitored and checked each maneuver. "Nice work," he offered, when Faulk had finished. His voice held admiration. Faulk thought so too. Despite the heavy pressurized gloves, he had operated the spacecraft with the same ease with which he had once flown the jets. With Apollo's burn chamber pointed toward the moon, they had to twist in their seats to see it.

When the timer indicated T minus 2 minutes, he spoke into the radio: "Apollo attitude ready."

"Cap. Com . . . Roger." Burke's voice came faintly.

"Two minutes to ignition," he finished.

"Check. Corrected data indicates a retrothrust duration of 5 minutes, 20 seconds."

"Roger, 5 minutes, 20 seconds." He cut off, studying his instruments. In the long plunge moonward, the earth's pull had slowed Apollo from an escape speed of slightly over 25,000 miles per hour to slightly under 500 miles per hour. Passing into the lunar gravisphere, it had accelerated again, now was hurtling through space at approximately 5,800 miles per hour, or nearly 8,500 feet per second. Retrothrust, programed to slow this speed to 5,250 feet per second along a planned reentry path, would allow the moon to capture Apollo in a 100-nautical-mile equatorial orbit. It was all very nice on paper. He only hoped it worked. At T minus one minute, he spoke: "Ready?"

"I've come this far," Mallon replied cheerfully. He had been in blithe humor since the talk with Lily Jordan.

Kovac, who had been shooting the stars, locked the sextant in place and inclined his head. As the timer hand reached zero, Faulk pressed the firing key. For a tense second or two the cabin was absolutely silent before the thunder from the engine came through the bulkheads.

"Slow in igniting," Kovac said uncertainly.

"About a second," he agreed, "but we're well within limits." As he spoke, he felt the G's, a force applied from front to back due to their rearward facing seats. The moon sped past as they hurtled toward its western horizon. Bleak mountains and craters flashed far underfoot as they decelerated, at the same time sinking under the moon's pull so that the effect was that of closing with the lunar surface in a shallow spiral.

"The Ocean of Storms," Kovac barked, expelling the words forcefully. "We're entering the dark side."

Oceanus Procellarum—the Ocean of Storms. It rang of music in Faulk's mind. Following the copilot's eyes, he glimpsed a tremendous plain broken here and there by rills, a few scattered craters and a low range of mountains. Flat, gridded, the bottomland reminded him of dry lake beds baked under a desert sun. Although predominately gray, occasional black streaks suggested basaltic outcrops without any pattern he could discern. He had seen close-ups of the moon televised by probes. There had been the same craters and seas, yet somehow they had held an unreality. This *was* reality, harsh and clear. In a way he couldn't discern, the difference between photo and eye was the difference between an abstract world and a physical one. He had *known* the moon was cratered and torn. Now he *saw* it. That spelled the difference.

Night rushed toward them, an enormous wave surging through space, speeding to engulf them. Beyond the Terminator, the border of night, the horizon cut black notches in the starfield. Under other circumstances, he decided, it would be beautiful. Then night was on them, not total night but a night washed in the pale light reflected from the earth. If the moon by day was stark blacks and whites, by night in earthlight it was blacks and creamy grays—fluid, malleable blacks and grays which constantly shifted, blotting out details. He had the eerie impression of staring downward at an earth desert under the light of a quarter-moon.

Kovac grinned through his faceplate and jerked his thumb downward, saying, "Our landing spot."

Faulk grinned back. "Think you can find it?"

"Get lost and you'll have a long wait," Mallon quipped. "They tell me it gets pretty cold down there."

"No sweat," Kovac replied confidently, then grew reflective. "We might sweat a bit getting back."

"We might," Faulk agreed.

"Depend on Lester," Mallon put in. "I'll be there to guide you . . . a beacon in the night."

"Beacon!" Kovac snorted.

"Listen for Lester . . . on the air everywhere. How's that for a slogan?" he asked.

"We'll be listening," Faulk assented. "Just be there."

Smiling, he turned his attention to the countdown clock. T plus 3 minutes and 20 seconds since ignition—2 minutes to engine cutoff. At the moment he felt comfortable despite the steady G pushing him against his harnessing. As the muffled roar of the engines continued, he riveted his eyes on the world from which they had come. It showed itself as a vast crescent, four times as great from tip to tip as a quarter-moon seen from earth. Due to its greater reflectance, it gave off fifteen times the light of a quarter-moon. Now the dark portion of the globe, easily visible, emerged gigantic in the firmament. Despite the distance, he felt he could almost reach out and touch it. Good to see—familiar, that was it. Earth meant people, friends, Karen and the kids—the good things of life. Even as a giant-darkened sphere in the heavens it stood as a symbol of those things. By contrast, the moon symbolized everything alien to man. Now, implacable and hostile, it seemed to gird itself for the assault from afar. Like marching against an enemy army, he reflected. The moon was a fortress whose donjons pierced the skies. Its defenses were erected of everything inimical to life. Against this foe they would pit themselves. Their warship? The frail shell of the Moon Bug. He grimaced, thinking his imagination was running riot. The counter hand was sweeping fast. *T minus one minute. T minus . . .*

The hand reached T minus zero time and he cut the main engine, sensing the immediate weightlessness and silence. The G-meter needle fell to zero, a certain sign they were in balance between the centrifugal and centripetal forces in which their orbital speed negated the moon's pull. Releasing suit pressure, he opened the faceplate, peering down into the night.

"Here . . . finally," Kovac exclaimed, sighing. "End of a three-day year."

"Rougher soldiering from here on out," Mallon remarked prophetically.

"That's for sure. We should be passing into the night-night."

"Come again?"

"The black night—the region beyond the earthshine. That's what I call it," the copilot explained.

"When the earth sets," Faulk injected.

Mallon laughed. "That's a new twist."

"Something we'll have to get used to," he agreed.

They fell silent, eyes fastened on the dark planetary crescent. The earth, plummeting toward the lunar horizon, disappeared; instantly, the landscape below them became a jet-black. It was, Faulk decided, as if he were looking into a black hole dug into the firmament. Cut off from both sun- and earthshine, the backside of the moon resembled the view one would get peering into a coal sack.

"Like speeding through a tunnel," Kovac observed.

"They used to have a ride like this at the amusement park," Mallon commented. "Little boats that drifted through a winding black tunnel . . . We used to take the girls."

"You'll be zooming through this tunnel quite a few times," the copilot responded, alluding to the solitary vigil the other would keep while he and Faulk rode the Moon Bug down.

"I'm an expert in dark rooms."

"Natch." As Kovac worked the radar scan, Faulk and Mallon talked over the mission. Both agreed the most critical period would be during lift-off from the moon and rendezvous with Apollo, a time which, in Mallon's words, would be like two butterflies trying to establish contact in a wind storm.

They were discussing it when Kovac exclaimed, "Blip . . . one of the communication satellites."

"Good," Faulk said, relieved. He had been hoping for this. Three of the satellites had been programed into lunar orbit in an effort to provide a reliable transmission relay to enable the Bug to contact Apollo when on opposite sides of the moon.

"There goes my sleep," Mallon groaned. "You fellows will be yakking all the time."

"Exploring the moon," Kovac corrected. "You'll do the yakking."

"Rub it in."

"Can you get a fix?" Faulk interrupted impatiently.

"It's higher—by 30,000 feet." Kovac studied the scope. "Slightly diverging course. Either its orbit is inclined to the equator or ours is."

"What do you think?"

"Too early to say, but if you're talking about a feeling, I think our flight path is pretty accurate."

"I feel the same."

"We'll know come dawn," Kovac promised.

"Let's hope that at least two of those babies are alive and working. We'll sure need them," Mallon declared.

"I'll settle for one of the three." Faulk smiled faintly.

At best they'd still have dead areas during which the Bug and Apollo would be out of contact. *Out of contact with Apollo—the world?* Doc Ashfield—all the space med men—had conducted numerous experiments on the effects of complete isolation. *The mind floated,* they said. *Disorientation came quickly, followed by hallucinations.* He couldn't quite imagine it. Still, he'd never be alone. There'd be Max. It would be worse on Les. No man in all history had ever been quite so alone as he would be. Did Les fear that time? he wondered. They fell silent, gazing into the night, a blackness of fantastic duration. A thin silver crescent lighted the edge of darkness as the sun nudged the horizon; almost instantly it became an intolerably brilliant disc against the ebon sky, speeding upward toward the zenith. In the normal course of a lunar day, it took the sun two earth weeks between rising and setting; the swift westward flight of Apollo reduced this length to sixty minutes. As daylight sped toward them, Kovac reached for the pelorus, an instrument for measuring angular distance. Faulk zeroed one of the timers. As the Terminator rushed under them at a ninety-degree vertical angle, he started it, then peered downward, watching the plain unfold as night fled to the rear. Kovac peered eagerly through the port.

"Still on the backside . . . the unseen side," he explained, "around longitude 140 east." Faulk craned his neck down at a broken land. Jagged rills marched across a vast plain edged by towering peaks. A flat, cracked area reminded him of desert lake beds. As the mountains sped under them and receded, the land became black, with splays of craters and sharp, grotesque hills. His eye discerned no pattern, unless it was that of randomness. Highlands, sea bottoms, craters and rills had been thrown together by a thoughtless nature. What, then, was the purpose of the moon? To ruffle the earth seas? Was it merely a handmaiden of earth, or did it serve a greater purpose? Or perhaps it was but a discard world, a handful of matter left after the sculpting of earth that had been tossed aside. He pondered it.

At T plus 16 minutes after crossing the Terminator, Kovac announced, controlling his voice: "We're headed into Mare Spumans, the Foaming Sea . . . about 90 degrees east longitude."

"Recognize anything?" Faulk masked his impatience.

"Not yet."

"Man, what a navigator." Mallon snickered. "Wouldn't be surprised to find we're on Mars."

Faulk glanced at the timer. "We're coming into the mapped side." He got on the radio, calling Cap. Com several times before the answer came.

"Cap. Com to Apollo—we read you."

Despite the spectral quality of the voice, he recognized Burke, asking, "You still there?"

"Overtime," the other replied cheerfully. "We need a union."

"Just emerged from a black, black night—now around 90 east," Faulk reported.

"Nice and sunny here."

"Sunny below us—about 250 degrees' worth."

"What's your altitude?" Burke asked.

"At 608,000 feet," Kovac cut in, reading the radar altimeter. "Almost 100 nautical miles. How's that for programing?"

"The double domes will be tickled pink. You should circle that ball of mud in two hours flat. Raise any of the com satellites?"

"One . . . in higher orbit," Faulk answered. "Max suspects its orbit is inclined slightly to the equator."

"That's how we figure it. What's it like below?"

Faulk described the surface, answering Burke's eager questions. "We'll tell you more later," he finally said. "We want to make some checks."

"We're plenty anxious, Joe."

"Later," Faulk repeated firmly. He signed off and zeroed another timer.

"Looks like a smear on the port," Kovac said conversationally.

"Where?" Faulk swung his eyes to the glass.

"Look carefully at the moon," he instructed.

Faulk studied the port glass, saw nothing unusual, then turned his attention to the plain, and saw a slight blurring he hadn't noticed before. "Counters don't show anything," he offered. Suppressing his perturbation, he inspected the other ports.

"Appears restricted to the forward viewing areas," Kovac finally observed.

"Radiation effects?" Mallon interjected.

"No, that tends toward discoloration." Faulk gazed speculatively at the copilot. "I'll inform Cap. Com. We'll have to watch it."

"Let's hope it's not cumulative." Kovac studied the instruments. "Velocity 3,557 miles per hour." He picked up the pelorus. Faulk watched the bleak landscape wheel by, from time to time taking pictures with a small hand camera.

After what seemed an interminable time, Kovac exclaimed excitedly, "There . . . Mare Crisium." He jabbed a finger toward a distant oval-shaped plain lying near the northwest horizon. "The Sea of Crises. You can't miss it. It lies between 11 and 25 degrees north latitude. . . ."

"We should spot crater Langrenus to the south." Faulk sensed an inner excitement, a fluttery feeling.

"They're there," the copilot said triumphantly. "Langrenus and Vendelinus . . . bordering Mare Foecunditatus, the Sea of Plenty." He took a bearing as Faulk watched the distant craters wheel by. "I'll signal when Langrenus passes 90 degrees abeam," he finished.

"Roger." Faulk moved his hand to the timer.

"Stand by. . . ." As the seconds ticked away, Kovac raised an arm, held it expectantly, then chopped it down saying sharply: "Mark!"

"Mark—timer on." Faulk flicked the key, at the same time starting an automatic camera which would make periodic film strips of the land fleeing beneath them. Consulting his charts, Kovac pointed out crater Taruntius at 5 degrees north latitude on the north shore

of the Sea of Fertility, and to the south, the huge crater of Gutenberg; beyond it a ragged line of cones marched poleward. Although
traveling only about one-fifth as fast as they had traveled in
earth orbit, the smaller circumference of the moon gave the impression of incredible velocity—mountains, craters and plains wheeled
toward them, whirling past and disappearing in the east.

"The Sea of Tranquillity," Kovac said. He spoke more confidently now. "Thirty degrees east longitude. Beyond are the Haemus
Mountains and farther . . . on the horizon . . . the Sea of Serenity." Faulk glanced at the timer—T minus 20 minutes since crossing
the Terminator—then back at a vast plain broken by innumerable
craters, crevices and rock formations contorted into unbelievable
shapes. From the height they appeared writhing over the ground
like serpents gone berserk. A chain of mountains rushed toward
them, its crags and spiny backbones encompassing a myriad of up-
land plains and rimmed valleys. Here and there he saw splashes of
ocher and brown, the first indication of color on the moon. He tried
to capture it on film. Enthusiastic, Kovac proudly named one land-
mark after another.

"There . . . Hipparchus, Albategnius and Ptolemaeus," he exclaimed suddenly, pointing to a great triangle formed of cones.
"And look . . . below . . . the Sinus Medii."

"Is that good?" Mallon asked.

"Means we're where we think we are," he responded. "Look at
its curving arm."

"Sounds like we're dead on the equator," Faulk observed.

"There, or very, very close," Kovac stated positively. "We'll
know if we pass over the crater Lansberg."

"We should be at . . ."

"Zero degrees, both latitude and longitude." He glanced at the
clock. "T plus 30 minutes—it checks."

As Sinus Medii hurtled to their rear, he pointed out the Sea of
Clouds reaching to the southern horizon, and to the north, the giant

crater Eratosthenes backdropped by an arm of the Apennines. Faulk smiled at his enthusiasm. Kovac's elation over the ease with which he located landmarks showed in his face and voice. Even Mallon seemed awed. Finally the copilot announced, his voice all at once sober: "We're heading into the Ocean of Storms."

Oceanus Procellarum. Faulk voiced the words silently. Envisioned by early astronomers as a storm-tossed sea, the vast tangle of rock and plain below him formed the greatest ocean plain on the moon's visible face; it also contained their selected landing site. He studied it intently.

"Copernicus." Kovac spoke with awe. Following his gesture, Faulk saw what appeared to be a huge cone rising from a plain that ended in a background strip of mountains. Although flattened by perspective, there was no mistaking that it was a crater, and a very large one. With Mallon crowding his shoulder, he studied it curiously. Its vast interior appeared terraced, resembling a series of concentric rings, in the centermost of which rose a number of smaller craters. Fixing his eyes on what looked to be streams of rock radiating outward from the cone in odd and contorted patterns, he suddenly realized they must be the mysterious "rays" which long had puzzled astronomers. Although dark, they glinted in the sun, reminding him of an oily river cascading downhill. He had seen similar igneous flows on earth, smaller but of the same apparent texture. He decided the crater was formed by volcanic action rather than any meteoric bombardment and made a mental note to pass the observation along to Cap. Com.

"What a hole!" Mallon exclaimed in wonderment.

"Fifty-five mile diameter . . . small compared with some," Kovac responded. "We should be sighting Lansberg. That must be Reinhold and . . . yes, there it is." Faulk spotted it at the same instant, an irregular saucer cupped in a spine of rock. He saw that they would pass almost directly over it.

"Small," Mallon observed.

"But important," Kovac rejoined. "She's smack on the equator."

"Mark it at vertical," Faulk ordered. Kovac nodded. As the crater wheeled under them, he signaled. "T plus 27 minutes from Langrenus," Faulk said, satisfied.

"Twenty-seven west longitude," Kovac affirmed. Their eyes met. "We're so close it scares me."

"Plunk on the equator," the copilot agreed. Faulk glanced back at the crater's terraced interior which held several secondary cones. From the nearly vertical view, it looked like a midget Copernicus. To the south the Riphaeus Mountains rose from the plain in jagged escarpments; beyond, nearly on the horizon, he sighted the crater Gassendi. The Terminator rushed to meet them. He got on the radio, impatiently waiting until Burke answered.

"We've crossed the main checkpoints," he announced, "dead on the equator."

"Good. How about some TV shots? Everyone's frantic for a look-see. *Life, Newsweek*—the whole damned press is here."

"Soon as possible," he promised. "We're checking out the run first, seeing what's below."

"Got your camera on?"

"We're mapping." Hesitating, he described the slight erosion effects noted on the ports. Burke showed instant concern.

"I'll alert the brass, see what they think."

"The lab boys would be better," he said drily.

"Sure, right away."

"It might not be cumulative."

"We hope. Keep a check. Let us know."

"Will do." He described Copernicus, giving his theory regarding the nature of the rays.

"I'll pass it along to the eggheads," Burke promised. "They'll regard it as umpteen billion well spent."

"Feel that way myself," he admitted.

"Know what you mean," the other replied. "I think most of the nation does, to judge from the reaction. You should see the mob, even the weeklies from North Burlap."

"Have you talked with Karen?" Faulk interrupted.

"And Eve and Lily," Burke assured. "We're in constant touch."

"And . . . ?"

"They're fine. Everyone's fine."

"Thanks, Whitey." He felt relieved.

"A regular NASA service," Burke responded grandly. "Don't mention it. Waco and Myers send their regards."

"Thanks, send ours . . . and to Phil Herndon."

"Will do," Burke promised.

Turning from the radio, Faulk relayed the message to the others.

"Good girls," Kovac said. "The poppas have the fun and the mammas get gray-haired."

"At least they know where we are," Mallon quipped. "That's something."

Staring through the port, Kovac announced, "Here comes the Terminator . . . and night." As Apollo rushed into the darkness, he gathered two sets of strip maps made by the automatic camera and laid them across the console.

"Time for school," he told Mallon.

"An apt pupil." The latter moved to his side. "Needless to say, I always inhabited the accelerated classes."

"Sure, sure," the copilot rejoined. "I just want you to get these landmarks straight in your head. It'll be nice to have you know where you are when we need you." As they turned their attention to the maps, Faulk turned to the port.

The night was black, alien, lonely. The surface below, seen only as a formless hulk that obliterated the stars, seemed infinitely far away. Peering down, he felt a wave of nostalgia. Thought of Karen and the children flooded his mind. She'd be sitting by the phone, one eye on the television, waiting for the latest word, all the time wondering how she'd explain to the children if he didn't come home. But he would. The resolve came with determination. It struck him suddenly how vast this world was, not in actual size but in its jumbled geometry. Craters by the thousands, great plains and seas, mountains that ran in all directions. It struck him, too, how little they could learn on this first trip—a bit about crustal formation and not much else. It would be decades, scores and scores of trips, before the moon yielded its final secrets. By then they'd be interested in Mars, Venus . . . The present trip was like a blind man trying to describe a forest through the feel of a leaf, he mused. Yet he would learn—not only about the moon, but how to land and live on a strange world, how to extract its secrets. He watched the earth drop toward the horizon. It moved faster and faster, then was gone.

When he looked back again, Kovac and Mallon were deep in their maps.

Chapter 7

"Oh, oh!" Kovac exclaimed.

Faulk raised his head sharply. "What is it?"

"The ports . . . they're really pitted."

Cursing softly, Faulk scanned the dawn line, now hurtling toward them. The view was fogged, not quite in focus. He returned his attention to the glass. Constructed in three layers designed to filter out harmful ultraviolet and infrared radiation, it held a natural darkish tinge, but this was different—more like a smeared windshield while driving on a foggy night. His eyes sought cracks or pits; finding none, he breathed easier. Yet there was no denying the gathering cloudiness.

"Looks frosted," he observed.

"The impact and erosion counters don't register anything," Kovac answered, puzzled.

"Could we have passed through a light meteoroid concentration?" Mallon asked.

"Should have registered," Faulk reflected. "I don't know."

"I was thinking of an even finer dust."

"Perhaps . . ."

"Could be," Kovac conjectured. "At fifty-two hundred feet per second, anything we hit—"

"We'll wait and see," Faulk interrupted. He swung toward Mallon. "Check the Bug, Les. Take a long look at the ports."

"Will do."

As the astronaut rose, Faulk got on the radio, repeating the call a number of times before Burke answered. When he finished his report, Burke said, "We just talked with the lab people. They believe it's meteoroid dust, even if the counters don't register. The brass is pretty excited. How's the Bug?"

"Les is checking it now."

"Let us know."

"Right away. Any suggestions?"

"How's your overall visibility?" Burke parried.

"Not too bad."

"They want a full report, Joe."

"There's no more to say, Whitey. Just the light clouding."

"I hate to tell you this"—Burke dropped his voice—"but you're not to attempt a landing until we see what happens. That's from the top."

"The longer we delay, the worse it gets," he objected.

"Orders, Joe. I'm sorry as hell."

"No one ever thought this would be all cake."

"It's not that, Joe."

"Okay," he replied wearily.

When he cut off, Kovac snapped, "We ought to soft-pedal it."

"We can't, Max. You know that."

"The glass isn't that bad," he expostulated.

"Not yet, but it might be."

"We could land the Bug on instruments," the copilot exclaimed savagely. "Lord, Joe, we're here. We can't let it get away now."

"I feel the same, Max. There's no argument there."

Kovac stared disconsolately through the port, watching the Foaming Sea sweep toward them. Worried, Faulk thought. Perhaps more than any of them, Kovac had his sights set on the moon. He wanted it himself, yet not so much that he would attempt a foolhardy landing as a last resource. The mission was far too valuable for that. Landing was secondary to returning Apollo safely. Herndon had stressed that point. Loss of crew and ship could inflict serious damage to NASA's program. Those were considerations Kovac discounted, he reflected. With the moon almost within grasp, he'd take any chance, no matter how slender. *Command*. The word seeped through his mind. He'd have to exercise it now—evaluate the risks and act accordingly.

When the eastern edge of Mare Crisium came into view, Kovac moodily said, "Langrenus coming up."

As he took a sighting, Faulk contemplated the possibilities. Clear vision was a must. Mallon would need an accurate view of landmarks to aid them in launch upward from the moon. They'd also need absolutely clear vision during reentry into the earth's atmosphere, a time when Apollo would be hurtling in at well over 30,000 miles per hour. More than that, vision was the most critical factor in landing the Moon Bug. As it was, they'd come down in the moon dusk of earthshine, with a visual field already reduced to a dangerous minimum. Add to that the possibility of dust storms kicked up by the Bug's exhaust— The complications were endless. Kovac raised an arm, chopping it downward.

"Mark!"

"Mark—orbital period exactly 121 minutes, 20 seconds," he

announced. "Right in the ball park. We'll double-check with Lansberg."

They discussed the visual problem until Mallon returned, reporting, "Slight glass damage on the forward ports. Not too bad."

"How about the view underfoot?" Faulk asked.

"Clear as glass," he replied, "and that's no pun."

"That's what we should tell 'em," Kovac stated emphatically.

Despite himself, Faulk smiled. Given no other way, the copilot would attempt an instrument landing. All he wanted was the go-ahead. Did that spell the difference between pilot and copilot? He wondered.

Crossing the narrow neck of the Sea of Tranquillity with the cratered highlands rushing toward them, they used the television camera, transmitting to Cap. Com. Kovac filled in with voice.

"Coming now," Burke reported ecstatically. "They're good, good. A bit patterned and distorted but good, much better than anything returned by the probes. I'm looking down at twin craters, an area of jumbled lava beds, or what resembles lava. The highlands drop off into a flat plain—"

"Sinus Medii," Kovac interrupted.

"Yeah, I can tell now. I can see Ptolemaeus to one side, Alphonsus, a whole line of craters. That must be Mare Nubium—"

"Check, you're looking southwest."

"Marvelous," Burke exclaimed. "Keep 'em coming. They're being rebroadcast . . ." The words spilled from his lips. "The shadows, they're fantastic. Some of the cones must be tremendous."

Finally Faulk called a halt. "Gotta get back to the navigation," he explained.

"When you get a chance . . ."

"Sure, we'll flood you with pictures."

"Starring Les Mallon," the engineer put in.

"We'll take 'em anyway," Burke promised. "They're really magnificent, Joe. Wish I was there."

As the moonscape fled past, Kovac made stellar fixes and trained his pelorus on a number of craters, transferring the navigational data to matched photo strips, one for Apollo and one for the Moon Bug. They also commenced a thorough check of the latter vehicle.

"Can't wait to get going," Kovac said.

During the ensuing hour-long night the pitting on the ports grew more severe; no one mentioned the fact. It was, Faulk reflected, a human trait—avoid the disagreeable; but he couldn't avoid it in his mind. It lay, deep in his consciousness, taking the form of a nagging anxiety which he was at pains to conceal from the others. From time to time he caught himself glancing at the glass.

On the following pass they concentrated on determining the surface characteristics of the Ocean of Storms adjacent to the Terminator in hope it would serve as a predictor of the lands beyond the daylight line.

"Crater distribution, cleavages, evidence of dust, gradient, surface smoothness—those are the things we want," Faulk stated.

"From this altitude?" Mallon asked incredulously.

"We can get an idea." He fingered a photograph made from earth during a daylight period. "This doesn't tell much."

"I don't believe craters will be a problem," Kovac surmised. "They're pretty sparse in this area."

"Large craters, yes. How about small ones?"

"This side of the Terminator's fairly clear." The copilot chewed his lip thoughtfully. "I don't imagine it changes much on the other side."

"On the moon?" Faulk asked dubiously. He had yet to get used to the sudden changes—the abruptness with which mountains gave way to seas, the odd distribution of rills and craters.

"Just a hunch," Kovac admitted. "Procellarum doesn't look too rough."

"I'm inclined to agree." Faulk studied the strip map. "We can't really say it's flat, though, Max. It could be plenty uneven."

"Quite a few rills," Mallon commented.

"I'm worried more over dust," he confided. "We can hover long enough to avoid rills and cleavages, but I'm not sure we can identify dust—or avoid it if it covers a large area."

"Your exhaust will kick it up . . . warn you."

"But will it tell us the depth?" Faulk faced him. "I don't mind a few millimeters or even inches, but several feet—" He swung toward the copilot. "How does the strip look to you, Max?"

"Dust," he said succinctly. "It looks too smooth for rock."

"Could be baked earth."

"You might have time to assess it on the way down," Mallon suggested.

"I doubt it," Kovac stated. "We'll still be plenty high when we cross the Terminator."

"An earthshine landing—who dreamed that up?"

"The eggheads," Faulk replied soberly. "It's that or a plus 250-degree temperature."

"Never tried it." Mallon grinned.

He looked at the copilot. "What's our exact flight time from Terminator to touchdown?"

"I plot it at twenty minutes to hover altitude," Kovac answered. "That's an outside figure."

"Add another two minutes," Faulk reflected. "We'll have to make some fast decisions."

"Amen." As he started to speak again, the radio came on.

"Your NASA correspondent," Burke said. Following Kovac's routine reports, he added: "The brass wants to know the status of the glass."

"Some additional pitting," he acknowledged reluctantly. "It doesn't impede vision to any great extent."

"How about the Bug?"

"In better shape."

"Think it'll give you any real trouble, Joe?"

"In the Bug? I don't believe so, Whitey. We won't be using the filter shades."

"How about Apollo? I'm thinking of the return trip."

"We already have that problem," Faulk pointed out. "A few hours longer won't make much difference."

"Good point. I'll pass the word," Burke said. "Stay in orbit."

"Stay in orbit," Kovac mocked when the radio fell silent.

"You can't blame Whitey."

"No, but you have to take chances somewhere along the line," he objected. "There's too much at stake to pull back now."

"They won't pull back," Mallon stated. "We're talking about a world."

"Do they know that?"

"You know it, Max."

"They know it," Faulk agreed. "They were planning this when we were flying kites."

"You sound confident," Kovac observed.

"I am, Max. I don't know why, but I am."

"Hope you're right."

While Mallon napped through the short lunar night that followed, Faulk and Kovac prepared the Moon Bug for descent. Although unable to gauge accurately the extent of window erosion during the night, Faulk had the impression the damage had increased; the stars appeared less bright, as if he were viewing them through a mist.

Kovac grudgingly agreed, but added, "There's still plenty of visibility."

"I won't argue. We're on the same side of the fence," he answered, "but we have to report facts."

"They'll make mountains out of molehills."

"Not with the stakes what they are," Faulk replied.

Kovac didn't answer and they continued their work. Checking the fuel, power and communication systems, they followed with a minute inspection of their personal gear—portable biopacks and oxygen canisters they would wear on the surface, flashlights, small hand tools, containers for rock and mineral specimens. Finally they inspected their suits—faceplates, heating elements, oxygen flow valves. Finished, Faulk grinned at Kovac.

"Ready, chum?"

"Plenty ready." Their eyes met wonderingly.

"It's been a long wait," Faulk said finally.

"Hopeless at times."

"It's past now, Max."

"Gives me a funny feeling," he answered. "Seeing the moon is one thing, but touching it . . ."

"I've thought of that."

"You ought to have a prepared speech."

"I'll leave that for the public information officer."

Kovac's face grew serious. "I'm still worried about the ports—what they'll say."

"Don't borrow trouble," Faulk advised. "Come on, we'll see what we can do with the brass."

When they returned to the Apollo cabin, the dawn line lay like a silver thread on the lunar horizon. The thread thickened and gathered speed. Engulfing plains, mountains and craters, it rushed to meet them. Mallon woke instantly.

"Short night's sleep," he commented. "Have the maid bring coffee."

"Out of the sack, Buster." Faulk gestured with his thumb. "It's Max's hour of bliss."

"Couldn't sleep if I had to," the copilot protested.

"You can and will," he replied firmly. "I'll conk out tonight." Winking at Mallon, he slipped into the pilot's seat, watching the Terminator flee beneath them. Ahead the land lay bright in a new morning. When he looked back again, Kovac was fast asleep.

Burke came on the radio and after Faulk gave his reports, asked, "How's the window condition?"

"Not too bad."

"More clouding?"

"Some." He hesitated to say too much.

"The lab people are puzzled why it only occurs on the night side," Burke explained.

"I have a theory."

"Shoot."

"I don't believe it's just a night phenomenon," Faulk offered. "The erosion's probably constant, but so gradual we don't notice the change till we hit daylight, then we see the cumulative effect."

"Sounds logical," Burke agreed. "I'll pass it along."

"Any decision yet?"

"On going down? Not yet. The top echelon is still in a huddle."

"What support do we have, Whitey?"

"Plenty, Joe. No one wants to pull out. It's just a question of safety."

"Sure, safety. Could I make a suggestion?"

"They'd welcome one."

"Why not make it a pilot decision? I'm in the best spot to judge safety."

"I suggested that," Burke disclosed. "They're kicking it around."

"If they think I have a hero complex, they can make it a crew decision. We won't go down unless it's unanimous."

"Pretty clever," Burke observed. "How do you think they'd vote?"

Faulk stated wryly, "You gotta admit it's democratic."

"Okay, I'll suggest it. The Bug all checked out?"

"Ready to go," Faulk replied.

"And you're talking about a vote." Burke chuckled.

"Max is ready to revolt," he warned.

"How about you?"

"I'm ready too."

"Okay, I'll warn 'em," Burke agreed. "I'll let you know what they decide."

"Do that, Whitey." He winked at Mallon. "I've got a hunch we're in."

Faulk slept the short night.

It began as they hurtled over the Terminator in the Ocean of Storms, ending an hour later as they raced toward the dawn line on the backside of the moon. It was a night turbulent with dreams. In them he rode a rocket sled across the desert sage, aborted the prototype Apollo, crash-landed a disabled jet. Burke, Waco, Myers, Herndon—their faces floated past. *Self-glory, Joe?* The dark eyes in Ashfield's gaunt, understanding face watched him compassionately. Karen and the kids. *Ride that beast, honey, ride that beast, ride that ride that ride* . . . He awoke, writhing, then abruptly straightened, staring at the backs of the others' helmets. It was very still and he had the impression they were sleeping. He lay back, listening to the thud of his heart, feeling a trickle of sweat roll down his cheek. Gradually the thudding diminished.

When he awoke again, it was to the sound of Kovac's voice: "Radio, Skipper."

"Right there."

"Burke with the morning news," the copilot reported, making way for him.

He slipped into the pilot's seat, saying, "Faulk here." As he spoke he glanced out, realizing the night had passed.

"Burke," the astronaut said in a clipped voice. "Here's Phil." He exchanged a quick glance with Kovac, waiting until the administrator came on.

After the usual amenities, Herndon asked, "How's the glass situation, Joe?"

"About the same."

"Pretty fair vision?"

"Not too bad," he answered truthfully. "What's the decision?"

"Pilot's decision," Herndon replied succinctly. "We're leaving it up to you, Joe."

"Thanks, Phil."

"The Chief is confident you won't take unnecessary chances," he added drily.

"Of course not."

"When can we expect a decision?"

"Right now," Faulk said firmly. "We're at go."

"Good." Herndon caught himself, and stemming his enthusiasm, added in his best professional voice, "I have confidence that it's a sound decision, Joe."

"Very sound," he replied gravely.

"Good luck," Herndon said, "and Godspeed."

"We'll be barreling back before you know it, Phil."

"I have confidence in that. Keep in touch."

"Will do."

"Well, whaddya know?" Kovac murmured as the radio grew silent. He looked pleased.

"I expected it."

"So did I," Mallon confirmed. "They can't afford not to have us go down."

Faulk didn't answer, feeling the impact of Herndon's message. He had expected it, yet somehow felt surprised. Nothing remained to be done but go down, he mused. It was the purpose of being here—to plant a human foot on the moon. Now they'd do it. He felt a growing sense of elation. His face must have revealed it, for Mallon's eyes danced and his lips were twisted in a grin. Faulk looked at Kovac.

"Let's go down, Max—give 'em the payoff."

"Bug to Apollo. How do you read me?"

"Loud and clear," Mallon replied. "How me?"

"Not too bright but clear," Kovac cut in. In high good humor, he sat shoulder to shoulder with Faulk in the Moon Bug.

Mallon disregarded the comment. "How do you feel, Joe?"

"Great."

"Max?"

"On top of the world, and that's no pun."

"Tapes on?"

"As of now." Kovac flicked a button to record all conversation for later transmission to earth, then glanced at Faulk. "All instruments at go," he added. Faulk acknowledged, studying Apollo. Coupled together nose to nose, the two vehicles sped through the lunar night at 175 degrees west longitude. Although Mallon faced him from the other vehicle, he discerned nothing save a shimmery gleam on Apollo's dark ports. Obscuring the stars, the vehicle's body blended with the night. Mallon spoke on the radio.

"Stand by for a time hack."

"Standing by." He eyed the clock.

"T minus 60 seconds"—the words came slowly, then—"Mark!"

"Mark," he responded.

"Report systems."

"All systems checked and ready," Kovac responded.

"Has Cap. Com cut in yet?" Faulk asked.

"Still blocked out," Mallon said.

"Roger." Faulk studied the control panel to bolster his memory of the key positions. Illuminated by faint red light to preserve night vision, they showed up as disconcertingly dim and close together. Fingering the controls experimentally, he wished the brains had come up with more flexible gloves. He made a last-minute check of oxygen settings and suit temperature. As the timer hand reached T minus zero, he fired small explosive bolts which freed the metal adapter binding the Moon Bug to Apollo. A second switch ignited a set of posigrade rockets which exerted a slight force, pushing the Bug free.

"Separation . . ." The slight jerk was followed by a widening gulf between the two spacecraft. For a moment Faulk allowed the Bug to move in yaw and roll, watching Apollo draw slowly away. Now, for the first time, he felt as if the dream had reality. The silence and darkness and sense of isolation stole pleasantly through his body.

"Smooth breakaway," Mallon reported. "You're in the clear."

Faulk gimbaled and fired the small reaction control jets, changing the Bug's flight path to a position off Apollo's bow. Kovac called the distances. At 500 yards he fired the jets again, correcting until the two vehicles maintained a steady distance between them.

"Bug holding steady," he reported.

"Steady it is," Mallon confirmed. The clownishness gone from his voice, he spoke in quick, terse words. "Check reaction control jets and report."

"Roger."

Faulk scanned the lunar horizon indicator before glancing at the power keys. A new type of rocket control, infinitely more precise than any before it, allowed special small jets to be fired either as a single burst or a chain of bursts at the rate of twenty per second. With combustion chambers smaller than peas and nozzles less than an inch long, a single burst from one of the engines lasted less than 500 millionths of a second. Burning a hydrazine fuel and nitrogen tetroxide oxidizer, each engine was capable of instantaneous thrust in excess of 50 pounds. At the instant of explosion, the flow of fuel and oxidizer stopped, starting again as the nozzle exhausted its burst of energy. He gimbaled a set of the jets and fired them, countering with another set as the nose began pitching forward. Stabilized again, he tested the vehicle in pitch and yaw.

"Handles beautifully," he reported. "Reaction control system operable and ready."

"Roger. Cabin pressure?"

"Four point two," Kovac replied. "Humidity 40 percent, carbon dioxide normal."

"Roger."

Faulk looked at the timer. Initiation of "go-down," scheduled for T plus 15 minutes from separation, still lay five minutes in the future. His eyes fixed Apollo. It looked monstrous against the stars. Aside from its array of antennas and saucers, it resembled a submarine miraculously set afloat in the space ocean. Unlike the Moon Bug, its lines were clean, designed for the fiery passage it would make back through the earth's atmosphere. He wondered how Mallon felt, alone above the alien sphere.

"You look good," Mallon cut in. "I have you steady in the scope. No yaw or pitch. Are you on automatic control?"

"For now. Will go off after start of go-down."

"How does she ride?"

"Like it was tailored for us," Faulk answered.

"Wasn't it?"

"You could say so."

"Coming on the range," Kovac interrupted crisply.

Faulk switched his eyes moonward, feeling a momentary vertigo. There was nothing there, absolutely nothing. A gulf, a void, a black abyss without name. Not till he switched his eyes and saw the black curve of the horizon against the starfield did he regain full orientation. Slowly, almost leisurely, he changed attitude in pitch and yaw, pointing the burn chamber in the direction of flight. Eyes fixed on the firmament, he waited.

"T minus 60 seconds," Mallon barked.

"Roger." He moved his eyes to the timer. Kovac picked up the count at T minus 10 seconds.

" . . . 8, 7, 6, 5 . . ."

As he reached zero, Faulk pressed the firing key.

Chapter 8

"Ignition!" Faulk spoke loudly as the whoosh of hot gases spewing from the stern tubes came through the bulkhead. A severe vibration transmitted through the seat set his teeth on edge.

"Roger." Mallon's voice came minute against the thunder of the engines. Kovac adjusted the radio. As the whooshing roar took on a steady beat, the vibration diminished. The force of retrothrust pushed Faulk against his harnessing, a gentle thrust in contrast with that during earth lift-off. Apollo began receding, slowly at first, then faster. Its velocity cut below orbital speed, the Bug began its long fall into a transfer ellipse that would establish it in a new orbit with a perigee 50,000 feet above the moon. This point, called *pericynthion,* offered the astronauts a last-chance escape should anything go wrong during descent. From 50,000 feet, the Bug's main engines could be fired, driving it outward to an intercept with Apollo on the opposite side of the moon. Faulk fully intended that nothing should go wrong.

"Commencing go-down," he reported.

"Roger, how does she handle?"

"Rough at first—like a dreamboat now."

"Looks like a fancy mushroom from here," Mallon returned. "I place us at 142 east longitude. See the dawn line?"

"Terminator? Not yet." He started to add something when the engines cut off, their function of slowing the Moon Bug accomplished. "Cutoff," he finished.

"On the nose. How's visibility?"

"Know better when we cross the dawn line, Les."

"I meant cabin light."

"Very dim. I'm playing the controls by feel. Gloves are awkward.

Wait'll I change attitude." Watching the horizon indicator, Faulk fired the small jets, bringing them into a feet-down position toward the moon. "Flight path in visual field," he ended.

"You can see?"

"By instrument. Is Cap. Com cut in?"

"Still blocked, Joe."

"Have you tried the relay satellites?"

"A few garbled words. We haven't got their orbital data pinned down well enough. I'll transmit the tapes to the Cape later, bring them up to date."

"You can put this on your tape, Les. Tell them we're ding-hao, copacetic, A-okay and all green," Faulk happily informed him. "On the way to a better world."

"Anything's an improvement," Mallon ventured.

"How do you feel, Les?"

"Being alone? No bother. Actually it's a promotion. I have my own command now."

"Delusions of grandeur," Kovac interrupted.

As they bantered back and forth, Faulk turned his attention to the port, watching the Terminator rush toward him. Whitey'd be sweating it out, he thought. They all would. Karen, Eve, Phil Herndon. Press and radio would have a field day. For some reason Doc Ashfield's face popped into his mind, his dark eyes mirroring the question: *Self-glory, Joe?* He smiled grimly. Whatever glory there might be lay far away. From here on out it'd be sweat, uncertainty, danger—the hostility of an alien world. The trick would be to stay alive. At the moment the glory appeared as dim as a sixth-magnitude star viewed on a foggy night. Twisting, he scanned the sky, spotting Apollo. Higher, it caught the morning light, glinting silver shafts.

The copilot had returned to shepherding the instruments, and for the moment quiet reigned. In the stillness Faulk's ear caught the faint hiss of oxygen passing through the suit valves, the click of a solenoid, a low hum in the phones. The new sound of life, he mused. The hiss-click-hum was the music of space, a new form of poetry. Mallon cut into his thoughts:

"How're your environmental readings?"

"Cabin pressure steady at 4.2," Kovac responded. "Humidity 43 percent, carbon dioxide normal."

"Your biomedical recorders on? The Cape will want readings."

"Are now." He flipped a switch. "What happens if I turn out to have high blood pressure?"

"They order you back and send me," Mallon replied. "Readings are coming through now. You can cut and send another take during the landing phase."

"Great, we'll have plenty of time."

"We'll frame a set for you," Mallon retorted. "Stop grumbling."

Kovac told him what he could do. Grinning, Faulk watched the plain unfold as daylight rushed toward them. After what seemed an interminable time, Mallon came on:

"I read you at 70,000 feet vertical from orbital plane."

"Check," Kovac affirmed.

"What's your above-deck altitude?"

"Now . . . 538,000 feet. We're picking up a fast sink rate."

"How fast?"

"I read it as 131 feet per second."

"About right," Mallon confirmed. "Glass okay?"

"It'll do."

As they ceased talking the silence returned, a deep stillness during which he had the sensation of hurtling through endless space—no, being suspended absolutely motionless in some dimensionless pit. As the dawn line sped beneath them, Kovac reported at altitude of 500,000 feet.

"How's your underfoot vision?" Mallon asked.

Faulk glanced down. "Stinks . . . too restricted."

"I meant clarity."

"Some clouding. Not too bad."

"More on this end too. It's going to be a dilly during reentry."

"I'll worry about that later," Faulk answered. He felt the silence again. This was the quiet time, he mused, the long drop. A fire drill —the fire would come later. Strange, he felt utterly calm, at peace.

Kovac studied the instruments, announcing, "Altitude 475,000 feet. Going down fast."

"Time?"

"T plus 13 minutes." The copilot consulted his instruments. "We're approaching 100 east, coming off the back of the moon. We should be hearing from the Cape."

"Three or four minutes," Mallon came in. A few moments later the radio crackled. "The Cape now," he reported. "Read them, Joe?"

"No, just a moment . . ." Faulk made an adjustment.

"Cap. Com calling . . ."

"Bug, I read you," Faulk interrupted.

"How's go-down, Joe?" Faint and ghostly, Burke's voice came from a world away.

"Fine, Whitey. Nice and smooth. How do you read me?"

"Some noise but okay."

"We'll have a breeze for a while . . . till we hit the 50,000-foot perigee."

"Give us full reports."

"Max has been. We're on the tapes."

"We want everything, Joe. Especially on the surface. Give us everything you see."

"Can't tell much till we get lower. Let you know soonest." Faulk glanced at the copilot. "They're burning . . . can't wait to find out what's below."

"I'm in the same boat," Kovac agreed. "Man, this is a slow trip."

"Yeah, but wait'll it picks up." Faulk gazed out the port. The moon swept past slowly, giving way to the stars as the Bug moved in roll, pitch and yaw. A pleasant, almost sensuous feeling stole over him.

Kovac must have felt the same, for after a while he remarked, "I could fall asleep."

Faulk let the vehicle revolve through several more turns, then reluctantly stabilized it and switched attitude control to the automatic mode. The surface below appeared unchanged—craters, mountains and plains wheeled slowly past, stark under the newly risen sun. The word "majestic" came to his mind. This was majestic but in an awesome sense. Tremendous seas that held no water, craters dead for countless millennia—cold, heat, eternal silence. A tomb world, he thought, the majesty of desolation. Somewhere down there they had a rendezvous. He strained his eyes toward the horizon. The Bug was dropping fast. He glanced at the timer, surprised to find that over thirty minutes had elapsed since initiation of go-down.

Mallon's voice broke into his ears: "Still there?"

"Where else?"

"Keeping in touch," Mallon explained. "How does she look?"

"The moon? Beautiful."

"Understatement," Kovac said reverently. "We're passing out of the Foaming Sea . . . looking almost straight down on Apollonius. There's a heck of a rugged range hemming the southern border of Mare Crisium. Looks like a topographical map in gray and black clays. You should see it."

"Where do you think I am?" Mallon queried.

"I meant Whitey."

"I'd love to see it, Max." Now, direct from Cap. Com, Burke's voice came stronger. Faulk caught his wistfulness. "How does Langrenus look from a lower level?" he finished.

"Sort of flattened," Faulk told him.

"See Gutenberg?"

"Coming up . . . a whole nest of craters," Kovac explained enthusiastically. He described the landscape fleeing past until Burke reluctantly broke in.

"Time for a check. Better fill us in."

As Kovac fed him the operational and enviromental data, Faulk kept his eyes on the lunar landscape. It struck him that in the short time they had been in orbit, he had come to know the moon very well. Its major landmarks already were old, old friends. Learning them from earth-made photo maps was one thing; here he knew them by minor details—odd-shaped craters, cleavages, small-necked bays, the contours of mountains and seas. There the Marsh of Sleep bubbled like a pancake, ended abruptly against the Sea of Tranquillity; Taruntius, with crater walls bearing the donjons of a castle. Standing between two sea plains, it resembled the kind of beleaguered desert fort he used to see in the Foreign Legion pictures. There marched the Pyrenees in rugged grandeur, its rock peaks embracing the shores of Nectaris. He had come to know this world. He reflected that even without the strip map he would be confident in his navigation.

He switched his gaze to the window glass, startled to find the fogging worse than his earlier observation had indicated. Starting to comment, he clamped his lips tight. Conceivably they could be ordered back into orbit from the 50,000-foot pericynthion. Unlikely as it was, he decided not to risk it. Like Kovac, he had committed himself physically and mentally to touchdown on the bleak surface spinning toward them.

"We're passing over Godin Crater," Kovac announced suddenly, "heading into Sinus Medii. Plus 41 minutes," he added.

"Is the shore as smooth as in photos?" Burke asked.

"A few indentures but fairly even. The coast of the Sea of Vapors is smoother . . . almost a perfect crescent. Can practically feel the waves."

"Beach . . . moon maids," Mallon said happily.

"There's an almost perfectly circular crater at the northern end
. . . Treisnecker. Wonder where it got that name?" Kovac paused.
"The land beyond looks bulged. Not a hill exactly, but more like a
bubble. You should see it, Whitey."

"Any chance of low-level TV?"

"Hand camera's the best we can do," he advised. "Hipparchus,
Albategnius and Ptolemaeus are on the other side. Plenty different
from down here. Looks like they were laid out on the vertices of an
equilateral triangle. That's rough area down there—stuff you can't
pick up on film. Never saw anything like it on earth."

"Can you spot the Hyginus Cleft?" Burke eagerly asked. "The
photos show it as somewhat like the Great Wall of China."

"More like a broken knife, I'd say. The slopes on this side look
smooth and hard as black glass, yet there's a sheen. . . . Somewhat
like sunlight on obsidian."

"I read your altitude at 220,000 feet," Mallon cut in. "Present
velocity and altitude will place you slightly downrange."

"An overshoot?" Kovac studied the board, then fed some calculations into the computer and read the results. "Need a velocity
cut," he told Faulk. "I'll feed you the figures."

Listening, Faulk gimbaled two of the heavy reaction jets in the
direction of flight. Trimming the Bug's attitude, he fired a short
burst, feeling the vehicle shudder under retrothrust.

The copilot consulted his board. "About right."

"Any heat buildup?" Burke queried.

"Slight rise in suit and cabin temperature. Nothing alarming."

"Have you tried to adjust it?"

"Not yet. We've been ogling the moon," Kovac replied. "I feel
like a blinking tour conductor."

"Better give it a whirl," Burke advised.

"Will do."

As he began adjusting the settings, Faulk studied the bleak land
below for some clue to the amount and distribution of dust—if the

creamy areas *were* dust, he reflected. They could be baked earth —almost anything. Many of the formations clearly were rock—gaunt, craggy, rising unpredictably as if strewn by a random hand. Great slabs lay at odd angles or jutted from the ground like weird leaning towers. Others took the form of mushrooms or kettles. They could be gigantic, or was he fooled by the clarity of an airless world? Clarity? It was a bucket of murk. He discussed it with Burke.

"It'll interest Ashfield," the latter declared. "That's the kind of dope he wants."

"I'm not worried about Ashfield, Whitey." He returned his eyes to the port, feeling the tension. Southward the area between craters Mosting and Ptolemaeus resembled bubbling caldrons that suddenly had solidified. Craters were everywhere, dotting sea and plain, and in the high uplands, often taking the form of rock-rimmed valleys of awesome depths. Several times he imagined he caught flashes of color—yellows, browns, ochers. And once a glimpse of pale green in the terracing of a small mountain crater. From time to time he took pictures with a hand camera. The plains largely were grayish-white except where splotched black by sun shadows, spinelike formations and the harsh grillwork of rills and crevices. Dust? He couldn't say.

"I see the Terminator!" Mallon exclaimed.

Kovac snickered. "Probably got the bed made down for a snooze."

"On the air everywhere—remember the slogan?"

"I'll call you every five minutes, make a check," the copilot threatened.

"If I don't answer, leave your name. The recorder will be on," Mallon promised. "See the Ocean of Storms?"

"The edge. It's moving in fast."

"Watch it," Burke put in. "See if you can pick up a clue."

"Will do," Faulk answered. He switched his eyes to the clock.

The drift of minutes. Odd, at times they skipped by at an appalling rate, tumbling one after another into the vault of eternity. At other times, like now, they passed with agonizing slowness. Why rush time? To get to the moon, or to get past the dangerous hurdle of getting to the moon? Or was it because, waiting, he felt helpless, as if he were an inconsequential pawn in the tumultuous game of win-a-planet? Or *was* the moon a planet?

Moodily he switched his eyes. For a while they were silent, watching the ground speed toward them. The Sinus Medii and intervening mountains dropped to the rear, and with them the bubbling pots and caldrons of Mosting and Ptolemaeus. A quadrature of small cones swept past as the apparent flatness of Procellarum rushed to meet them. Grays, whites, blacks—a flatness and yet a mosaic that spoke of heights and depths, slashing shadows that hinted of bottomless gulfs. This was Procellarum, the vast ocean where the Bug would touch down behind the curtain of night.

"I see the Terminator!" Kovac exclaimed.

"What's it like?" The suddenness of the question revealed Burke's eagerness. Faulk felt sorry that he wasn't along.

"A black thread . . . no, a rope. It's like a black river flooding over the plain," Kovac said hesitantly. "Damned odd, it has a spreading motion like a wave after breaking, washing up on the beach. Man, look at it come toward us!"

"Fast," Faulk supplied, "and black. I can't see earthshine behind it."

"Your eyes will have to adjust," Mallon interrupted. "You should have your red filters down."

"Check." Kovac pulled the filter shade and instantly the ground below took on a deep reddish hue that washed out the roughness of the plain, giving it a more level look.

"Can you still see the Terminator?" Burke queried.

"Through the filters? As a big dark wall," Faulk answered. "It's rushing toward us at tremendous speed."

"Flick up your shade as soon as you hit it," he warned. "Don't look back into the light."

"Will do. The filters tend to flatten the plain—hide the roughness."

"You'll adapt," Burke advised.

"It's a fantastic sight, Whitey." Faulk groped for words. "The plain has a grayish color . . ."

"Ash?"

"Can't say, but it has an odd pattern, almost as if it were . . . undulating."

"Sounds like rolling land, Joe."

"I'm not certain. The gray is uniform in places. Then, suddenly, come the black areas—real odd shapes. They could be rocks or shadows cast by low hills. They could be anything, Whitey."

"Try to get an idea before you hit the night line."

"I'm trying, Whitey." He fell silent, staring ahead, watching the engulfing night sweep toward him. Here and there small notches appeared at its lower border and as quickly vanished. He realized it was the effect of the night line overriding the craters. Copernicus and Kepler wheeled by in the north. Southward, the Riphaeus Mountains, bathed in light, stood as a last bastion against the curtain of night speeding toward it over the Ocean of Storms. The silence grew tense, almost electrical, and with it Faulk had a growing realization of the problems they faced. Night, craters, surface cracks, dust—as his mind conjured a picture of total disaster, his uncertainty grew; with it his confidence evaporated, leaving him drained and tired. He set his jaws, staring ahead.

As if reading his mind, Kovac remarked, "All the elements of a third-rate thriller."

Despite himself, Faulk chuckled and immediately felt the tension commence to melt. Good old Max. His remark suddenly placed everything in a different perspective. This was just another job, another vehicle to be tested. And that's what he was—a test pilot. The jitters were nothing to be ashamed of. They all had them. Even Kovac, he suspected, could he see behind that stoic mask. To hell with it. He'd take her in, come hell, high water or dust, just as he'd taken other test jobs in. No May Day yet. He was sorting his thoughts when the line of night swept in, engulfing them.

"Terminator." He flipped up the filter shade, straining his eyes, in the first few seconds seeing nothing. "Black, very black," he reported.

"You'll adjust in a minute." That was Mallon, his voice surprisingly clear. "We'll make a note that copilot failed to pull the filter shade in time to allow full visual adaptation. I expect it'll be reflected in the next fitness report."

Faulk grinned at Kovac's epithet, but noted that his eyes were beginning to detect formless patterns—deep tans and blacks, a mixture of movement.

"Vision adapting," he said tersely. "It's a dark deck, dark tans and blacks."

"Earthshine," Mallon said.

"Can't really see anything yet. How about it, Max?"

"Vague details. We're still high."

"Light areas should be the safest," Burke broke in. "What kind of patterns do you get?"

"Twisted, Whitey." Faulk scanned closely. "There is no pattern, just a splash of gray—no, more of a cream. The lower we get, the creamier it looks. But there's plenty of black too. It must be a doozy."

Mallon warned crisply, "Watch your instruments."

"Glued to 'em," Kovac responded. "Near 60,000 feet. Plenty of elbow room."

"Not for long," Burke cut in. "You have a helluva high sink rate."

"Watching it, Whitey. We cut forward velocity."

"Roger, standing by."

"Standing by," Mallon echoed.

The moon rushed toward them at an appalling rate, a mask of pale light blotched by great formless shadows. They danced and shimmered with an odd fluid motion, reminding Faulk of the times he had buzzed the Pacific at night in jets. The light areas here were like moonbeams seen on waves, the spume rolling down into the troughs, spindrift on the wind. Far ahead he glimpsed a faint horizon line, scarcely more than a dark arc slicing the heavens. Twisting, he looked toward earth. It hung in the sky, a slender pale crescent.

"Fifty-five thousand," Kovac said, hunched toward the instrument panel.

Faulk didn't reply. The eggheads said he would have vision comparable to that during a desert night under full moon. He had seen many such nights—sand dunes, rocks and dry lake beds formed recognizable landmarks. At times he could even distinguish sage, the grotesque arms of joshua trees, ocotillo. But this was like no desert he'd ever seen. Creams, grays, blacks—a weird mixture of contrast and form. The inability to discern meaning baffled him. The black splotches were . . . what?

"How's your vision?" The terse question revealed Kovac's concern.

"Not good . . . not bad."

"The glass or the light, Joe?"

"Can't tell. I think it's a bit of each. This earthlight's for the birds."

"It should pick up," Kovac said, without changing his hunched position. He reminded Faulk of a gnome.

"It will." He spoke reassuringly, then wondered whom he was trying to reassure—himself or Kovac. Studying the horizon indicator, he corrected attitude and aligned the burn chamber for retrothrust.

In no time at all Kovac said, "Fifty-two thousand."

The radio crackled and Mallon came on. "Fifteen hundred feet to the point of no return. Vision any better?"

"Not so you could notice," Kovac snapped tersely.

"You can kick her back into orbit at pericynthion—"

"Nuts."

"Natch, but I have to request a decision."

"We're going for broke," Faulk answered.

"Fifty-one thousand," Kovac said. "Can't see a thing."

"The white areas might be better than the black if you have a choice—"

"If we have a choice." Kovac scrunched forward as if to see better, and a short time later said, "Almost 50,000."

"We should be around 40-41 west," Faulk broke in.

"By the timer," Kovac amended. He spoke into the radio: "Can you give us a bearing, Les?"

"On the clock you're around 41 west, perhaps a bit less. You're at plus 58 minutes."

"Thanks, but time doesn't make a bit of difference."

"Nurse your fuel. . . ."

"Like mother with child," the copilot said. "Still like to trade places?"

"Not at the moment," Mallon replied candidly. "Standing by."

"Near perigee," Kovac announced. The silence swept back and he added: "Pericynthion . . . 50,000 feet."

Faulk looked at the dimly lit consoles and controls. Fifty thousand, the point of decision. He could change attitude, kick back the main engines and intersect Apollo's orbit for rendezvous. Or he could go down. He looked out. The cream and shadows areas were whirling past faster, seemingly less distinct than before. The lower he got, the worse it got. It would be like trying a dead-stick jet landing on some wild stretch of desert. Darned near an instrument letdown. Shifting his eyes, he flashed a glance earthward. A silvery crescent, it rode serenely through the firmament, heedless that two of its children were entering the alien hell of its outcast moon. Karen! For an instant he glimpsed her profile carved in the limb of earth. *Ride that beast, honey.*

"I'll ride it, baby." He spoke subconsciously.

"What?" Kovac shot the question tersely.

"Nothing, didn't say a thing," he denied, abashed. He took a last look at the sky. Bluish Sirius, the giant Canopus a yellow-white against the night, the reds of Betelgeuse and Antares—stars he had followed from a hundred places on earth while with the Marines.

"Pericynthion," Kovac repeated.

He looked at the copilot. "Ready?"

"Let's go," Kovac said tightly. "Take her in."

"Standing by for go-down."

"Roger." Mallon's voice came faintly through the phones.

His hand poised, Faulk hesitated as he checked the Bug's attitude, then pressed the firing key. "Ignition," he called.

"Roger."

He felt the sudden retrothrust. "Main engines firing. We're on final go-down."

"Roger. Watch it."

"Watch it yourself. Is Cap. Com on the hookup?"

"Unless he's on a coffee break."

"Read you, Joe." Burke's voice was broken and slurred. "Give it all you've got."

"Will do, Whitey."

"Standing by."

"Standing by," Mallon echoed.

Kovac scanned the instruments. "Ninety-nine percent fuel."

"Good, let's use it up." As he spoke, he felt the gathering G forces. Go-down. Go-down. He stared out. The black-white moon rushed toward them.

Chapter 9

Down, down . . .

Blackness, the thunder of retrofire, sharp vibrations, the dance of red lights on the instrument panels—Faulk had the eerie impression of swinging in pitch and yaw while hurtling moonward out of control. It was the vertiginous feeling of skidding around corners, riding a super roller coaster—swerving, climbing, falling with such rapidity that all motions congealed into one. Dropping at an appalling rate, the sudden braking gave his body a logy feeling, drained the blood from his head and dimmed his vision. He shook his head, struggling to clear it, conscious of the constricting suit.

"A real go-down," Kovac gasped.

"It'll let up." He squinted through the lower port toward the touchdown pad; the harsh glare of exhaust gases beyond the engine skirt blinded what little sight he had left and he jerked back his head, staring fixedly at the black night in an effort to regain dark adaptation. Luminous after-images floated through his visual field. He blinked rapidly to clear it, then got on the radio and advised Burke of the problem.

"You'd better mark that in the book for future designs," he ended.

"One of you will have to maintain dark adaptation," the other said swiftly. "Have Max shield his eyes."

"And if I'm blinded?"

"I'd say try it on instruments, Joe."

"An instrument landing—yesterday we thought that a joke."

"Hope it doesn't come to that," Burke replied solemnly.

"Don't sweat it out. We'll make it."

"Roger. Standing by."

"Forty-nine thousand feet," Kovac rasped. "Ninety-seven per-cent fuel. We sure put the brakes to this buggy."

"Can't see a thing, Max."

"Attitude, sink rate . . . we're okay." Kovac hunched closer to the instrument panel.

"Watch attitude till my eyes clear," Faulk instructed, then forced his voice to a calmer level: "Don't look through the lower port. There's one heck of a glare."

"So I gathered. We're passing through 47,000 . . . fuel at 96 per-cent."

"Feels hot."

"Suit temp's a bit high, about 87 degrees," Kovac said. He began fiddling with the setting. "I'd hate to give the doc a blood pressure reading now."

"That's for sure." Staring into the night, Faulk's vision began to return. Slowly the stars came back with former clarity, filling the sky like luminous baskets; downward, the milk and black patterns of the moon emerged. As his vision grew stronger, the vertiginous sensation passed. The vibrations had abated and the engine had a steady roar. He brought his thoughts into focus. He could bring the Bug to hover a few feet above the ground. Barring extreme rough-ness, the radar altimeter would allow an accurate approach. He had the search beams. Given a minute or two of hover, he could pick a flat spot. If there were a flat spot. And if there were no dust. He let the thoughts flow. From time to time Kovac called out al-titude and the percent of fuel remaining in the descent tank. He held a taut posture, his eyes on the instruments.

After the first moments Faulk realized the strangeness had passed. He felt as though he were in the cockpit of a jet during night maneuvers. There were all of the same elements—pressure suit, dimly lit panels, radio voices, small cramped quarters, the in-cessant muted thunder which after the first few moments the ear refuses to hear. But it wasn't a cockpit, at least not on a jet fighter.

He couldn't get lulled into that security. This was a spaceship, a mite in the skies of an alien world. Instead of long paved runways there was . . . what? Rock, dust, a yawning slash in the ground or unseen peak. Or would he luck out, land on a smooth flat plain? Darn the vision.

"How goes?" Mallon's query, terse and clipped, revealed his anxiety.

"Twenty-five thousand feet, 54 percent fuel," Kovac responded.

"Better hoard some for hover."

"We're trying, Buster."

"I'm holding you on the scope. How's your vision?"

"Lousy," Faulk cut in. "The glare from the lower port will give us real trouble."

"Your landing lights might override it," Mallon hopefully suggested.

"Or blind us worse."

"How's your overall vision, Joe?" The voice was Burke's.

"Not so good."

"Glass worse?"

"Can't say. I suppose some of it's the low light level."

"How well can you see?"

"Enough to get by, we hope. All depends on what happens lower down."

"What's it like below?"

"The moon? Formless patterns, black and cream. Can't really distinguish between them. There's movement, or appears to be. Don't know whether the blacks are rocks or shadows."

"Stick to the cream, Joe."

"If it's not dust."

"The eggheads don't anticipate it, at least not a deep layer."

"The eggheads aren't riding this crate down," he returned emphatically. "I can't take a chance on theories."

"Use your judgment, Joe."

"Yeah, and hope it's right."

Mallon interrupted. "Procellarum looks pretty flat from here. Can't see much in the way of shadows, Joe."

"Not at your altitude, Les. This is small stuff."

"Fast go-down," Kovac interjected. "Twenty thousand feet, 43 percent fuel. We need an economy model."

"Nurse it," Burke anxiously instructed.

"Roger, Whitey." Faulk saw the ports had become more blurred than ever. He reported it crisply for the record, adding: "It's from the engines. We're going down through the plumes."

"Try throttling back."

"Am doing." He reduced thrust to 75 percent of maximum power and the swirling motion seen through the glass diminished. "Some improvement but still lousy," he reported.

"Might improve," Burke supplied hopefully.

"Nothing's improved yet," Kovac returned. "We're at eighteen thousand."

"Any improvement in fuel consumption?"

"Too early to say." The talk subsided and Kovac scanned his instruments, then stared out the port. Suddenly he jerked erect. "Looks like small cones down there."

"Great." Faulk's eyes caught them at almost the same instant: small circular and elliptical bands strewn randomly over an area edging their flight path. Dark uneven splotches suggested ragged hills and outcrops. "Craters," he said tersely.

"Shouldn't be," Burke responded. "You on course?"

"Think so," Kovac answered. "I'm judging by clock and altimeter. No time for a stellar fix. How about it, Les?"

"Have you on course," Mallon replied.

"We can't be far off."

"Maps indicate area clear," Burke persisted.

"This is small stuff—probably didn't show," Faulk interceded.

"Could be," Burke acknowledged.

"Fifteen thousand feet, 35 percent fuel," Kovac continued. "We're gaining a bit on reduced thrust."

"Good. Watch it," Burke instructed. "Am standing by."

"Roger."

Squinting through the port, Faulk cursed his faceplate, the swirling engine plumes, the dark glass, the blurring. Like Kovac said, it had all the elements of a slapstick comedy. Everything that could happen was happening. They'd anticipated a few hazards but not . . . this. He strained his eyes, aware of a taut, tingling feeling in his scalp. The familiar tightness. The moon was a medley in creams and blacks, writhing shadows playing hopscotch. Here and there long black slashes brought visions of gaping fractures in the moon's crust. Realizing the picture his mind had conjured, he forcibly dismissed it.

Finally, Kovac announced tautly, "Ten thousand feet, 27 percent fuel."

"We're gaining."

"Sink rate 54 feet per second," he ended.

"Can you predict how much hover time we'll have?"

"Depends on our maneuvering. Not more than a couple of minutes—maximum."

"During final letdown I'll have to risk the glare. Stand by to take over, Max."

"Will do."

"But don't look down. If it blinds me, it'll blind you. You'll have to try it on instruments."

"Roger," the copilot agreed.

"Tape every move," Burke warned.

"Will do."

"I'm keeping them on the scope," Mallon broke in. "Do you want me to send positions?"

"You'd better," Burke decided. "All the data you can tape."

For some reason Faulk had a momentary vision of Mallon's

lonely ride through the black lunar night, with the only company the remote voices on the radio. If anything happened to the Bug, Les could have one rough trip home. He shook aside the thought, and peering into the night, became conscious of some subtle change in the surface below. He tried to pin it down but failed.

"Forgetting the clock," Kovac said suddenly, "we're about three minutes from hover . . . a bit less."

"Check." He studied the landscape a moment longer, then reported, "Shadows seem flattening."

"More cream than black?" Burke asked.

"Perhaps. I can't say exactly. It just doesn't look as rugged."

"Flatter?"

"Can't say. Some of the cream areas appear larger."

"Pick out the biggest one, Joe."

"Will try, Whitey. The glass is pretty blurred, gives everything a smoothing effect."

He stopped talking to peer ahead. From high altitude the moon had appeared racing toward them. Now the picture had reversed and they were hurtling over it, hurtling and dropping. He fought his harnessing to lean closer to the port, conscious of the blurred glass. There a small crater, here a hill, a crevice, a milky rectangle that looked absolutely smooth and rock-hard—he absorbed the details, trying to find a common denominator, something which would enable him to judge land contours in the vicinity of touchdown. He found none. This was a tangled, discordant scape, unpatterned, formless, unpredictable, shaped in now dead eons and unchanged by wind, rain or erosion. Baked by day, frozen by night, and bombarded by meteoroids and the sun's ultraviolet rays, it was a grotesque parody of a world. Yet its bleakness gripped his imagination. This was an inferno without fire, a hell, the architecture of a maddened nature. The House of Lucifer.

He was contemplating it when Kovac spoke tightly: "Seven thousand feet, 23 percent fuel."

"Sink rate?"

"Fifty-one feet per second."

"Did you get that, Whitey?"

"Roger, you should be close to your landing area, Joe."

"Confirm," Mallon requested.

"I'll go into early hover, see if I can jockey for you," Faulk decided.

"Good idea," Burke asserted. "Standing by."

"Standing by," Mallon echoed.

Faulk adjusted the throttle and cut back on descent speed. His earlier uncertainty and tension had vanished; he felt an icy calm. This was his baby. Kovac could help with the readings, advice, handle the radio—no one could help with the controls. That went for Mallon, Burke, the whole hierarchy of NASA. Nothing counted now but precision, judgment, prompt and correct reactions to whatever emergencies might arise. And there would be emergencies; he couldn't expect a smooth textbook landing in this world. But it was in his hands, absolutely, with a finality guaranteed by the clock. The point of no return, vanished into history, was not even of academic interest.

"Altitude 5,000, fuel 19 percent, sink rate 46 feet per minute."

Kovac snapped the words with an edge Faulk hadn't detected before. He glanced at him once, quickly. The copilot was hunched forward, his face scant inches from the control panel. The red lights against his faceplate gave his eyes a satanic look, the more so from the fatigue they mirrored. The one quick look sufficed to tell him that Kovac had shut out the moon. His universe had become the small world illuminated in red—instruments that gave such things as speed, rate of descent, glide angle, attitude, fuel consumption. But it wasn't from fear or uncertainty that he had shut the door on the moon; it was the utter concentration his job demanded, the absolute accuracy of each figure he gave. Faulk understood that Kovac's ability to concentrate on a handful of square inches while an out-

land world rushed toward him reflected the copilot's confidence
in him. He'd made a good choice, a *very* good choice, Faulk
considered. Win or lose, he couldn't have picked a better man. He
owed it to Kovac to win.

"Altitude 4,000, fuel 18 percent . . . a trifle less. Sink rate 43."

"Approaching hover altitude," Faulk reported.

Roger. Roger. The two voices from two different worlds tinkled
in the phones a second or so apart. The quickness and terseness of
the responses told him of the pressures the others felt. He had a
fleeting vision of Burke hunched over the radio with Ashfield,
Herndon, the upper crust of NASA, hovering around, waiting for
the word from space that would tell them how well they'd planned,
how well they'd built. And what kind of a pilot they'd picked, he
thought grimly. Deliberately he forced himself to relax.

After what seemed an interminable time, Kovac said tightly,
"Two thousand feet, fuel 15 percent, sink rate 38 feet per second."

"Roger." Faulk made a quick adjustment in sink, gimbaled and
fired a jet, as quickly trimming with another. The Moon Bug swung
slowly, pendulously in pitch, bringing the main burners into firing
alignment.

"One hundred and three feet per second horizontal velocity,"
Kovac barked.

Faulk nodded. In effect they were skidding sideways across the
lunar surface. Gimbaling the large reaction control jets, he fired
several short bursts. The Moon Bug bucked and shuddered. He
had the impression of standing into a gale. The attitude indicator
showed a yaw movement and he corrected it. "Forty, thirty . . ."
The copilot tolled their speed as Faulk made further corrections,
conscious of the scant amount of fuel. Finally the copilot reported
zero horizontal velocity.

"Altitude?"

"Sixteen hundred fifty."

"Altitude sixteen fifty," Faulk repeated in the phones. "Zero horizontal velocity. Descending to hover position at . . ." He hesitated.

"Thirty-three feet per second," Kovac supplied.

"Sink rate 33," he repeated. *Roger. Roger.* "It's fast but we're burning the fuel . . . gotta get down. Keeping eyes off lower port to preserve dark adaptation. Visibility poor. Light and shadow, not much definition, can't assess landing area . . . depending mainly on instruments." He spoke quickly, conscious of the importance the moment held for the record. There'd be other teams, other ships, other landings. Every scrap of information was vital.

"You should have 8 percent fuel at final hover before touchdown," Burke interrupted. "You'll need it, Joe."

"Won't have it."

"Fifteen hundred feet," Kovac said. "Fuel 14 percent, sink rate 28." Faulk gimbaled the attitude jets downward to provide additional retrothrust and fired them. "Sink rate 30 . . . 27 . . . 24 . . . 19 . . ." Kovac intoned slowly. As the jets cut off, he finished: "Sink rate constant at 15 feet per second."

"Fifteen feet per second sink rate," Faulk reported. *Roger. Roger.* "The ground patterns have stabilized a bit . . . not the apparent motion . . . but I can't make out definite detail. Shadows all different shapes . . . indicate roughness, but that's just a guess. A few of the light areas are elliptical. Might be small craters. There's an odd sort of grid pattern . . . like the floor of a desert dry lake. We're at . . ."

"Eleven hundred and thirty," Kovac supplied quickly.

"Eleven thirty feet with zero horizontal velocity. Bug handles very well. No trouble with attitude control; no trouble at all except with downward view and glass erosion. I'll cut sink rate to hover at 600 feet." He throttled up.

As he paused, Mallon cut in: "Can you flip your biomed switch . . . give the doc his readings?"

Kovac complied. "Biomed on."

"Roger."

"Moving down at 15 feet per second rate," Faulk reported. "Searching for best touchdown spot. Real murky below. Even the cream color is murky but I see blacks, the blacks of rocks."

"Stick to the cream," Burke barked.

"Trying . . ."

"Altitude one thousand," Kovac cut in. "Fuel at 9 percent . . . a trifle under." He cut the biomed switch, peering at the instruments.

"Moving down, handling nicely," Faulk informed. "No trouble with vehicle, none at all aside from vision. Definitely need more downward glass . . . some way of whipping exhaust glare. Plumes still a problem. There's a large creamy patch just off to the right. That's north. I'm giving her some horizontal sweep." He gimbaled the nozzles of the small jets and fired a short burst. "We're moving toward the patch slowly . . ."

"Twenty feet per second horizontal velocity," Kovac interrupted. "Sink rate 15 feet per second . . . just passed 700-foot altitude."

"Patch looks odd," Faulk took up. "It's sort of elliptical but squared off at one end . . . has a ragged dark slash through the center. Other slashes near far border . . . think they're crevices. Will steer clear. Cream area might be ash. Can't quite tell. Looks around a hundred yards through longest diameter . . . runs same direction as our flight path. Surrounding area splotchy. Nothing high but looks extremely rugged."

"Five hundred feet," Kovac said crisply. "Fuel 7 percent."

"Coming to hover . . . should be over east border of patch." Faulk fired the jets, correcting with several short bursts. "Zero horizontal velocity. Yes, I can still see the farther edge of patch. Looks definitely lighter than surrounding areas. Aside from the one ragged shadow, I can't see any texture . . . nothing to indicate composition. Looks smooth. I'll pass over laterally, look at it from the other side." He fired the jets again and within a few seconds Kovac chanted:

"Fuel at 6 percent. Ten-feet-per-second horizontal velocity. Fifteen . . . twenty . . . twenty-five . . ."

Faulk cut back the power. Watching through the rear port, the edge of the patch came into view and commenced receding. As the dark slash came into sight, he braked with the small jets, bringing the Bug to hover just beyond the west border of the patch.

"Fuel 5 percent," Kovac said crisply.

"Still can't tell," Faulk said tensely. "Have an idea it's ash but don't know why. The shadow across the center looks more like a crevice than a ridge. Can't say why but it looks that way. I'm going down to a hundred feet." He adjusted retrothrust.

"Watch it, Joe. Might be a peak," Burke warned.

"Watching . . ."

"Ten feet per second," Kovac snapped in a brittle voice. "Fuel near 4 percent." Faulk didn't answer, intent on the patch. It could be solid, ashy, almost anything, but aside from the single dark slash across the middle it appeared relatively smooth. A suspicion nibbled at the corner of his mind. He saw no shadows to indicate heights. "Four hundred feet," Kovac intoned, and after a while, "Three hundred."

"Earthshine isn't as bright as it's supposed to be," Faulk cut in. "Definitely less light than full moon on the desert. Still can't discern detail except the dark area looks more and more like a crevice. I'd say it's pretty wide . . . six or eight feet. I'm afraid to use the beam; won't till I have to." He paused. "Weird, Whitey. I'm below three hundred feet and still guessing. Looks bad."

"Better pick a spot," Burke said edgily.

"Trying, Whitey."

"Two hundred feet," Kovac interrupted. "Fuel 3 percent. Sink rate—"

"Getting low on fuel," Faulk broke in. "Can't tell much about area around patch except that surface is smooth. Can't see signs of rises except near borders. It could be convex or concave . . . possibly even flat. Got a nasty suspicion."

"Ash?"

"Yeah, could be deep."

"Steer away from that, Joe."

"Where? No choice. Big rocks at the border. Still moving down."

"One hundred feet," Kovac called.

"We're at a hundred. I'll hover and switch on the landing lights— risk a look through the lower port. If I blind myself, Max'll bring her down on instruments."

"Good luck!" The words came over the radio, but whether from Whitey or Les he couldn't say. He halted their downward movement, flicked a switch and, studying the lower port, swept the beam toward the far edge of the patch. The ribbon of light uncoiled, making an unbroken silver road across the patch.

"Doesn't show a thing through the forward port. I'm looking down." He adjusted the light and squinting, peered through the lower port at the single touchdown pad in view. For an instant his eyes felt dazzled; he looked long enough to see that the beam revealed nothing except a single brilliant ellipse where it struck the patch. He looked back, blinking rapidly in an effort to clear his vision.

"Can't see a thing . . ."

"Blinded?" someone asked.

"Some, the light doesn't show anything. Just a glare."

"Protect your eyes."

"How?"

"Two percent fuel," Kovac announced.

"Fuel getting low. I'm going in . . . sweep area with exhaust." He throttled back, simultaneously gimbaling and firing the attitude-control jets. At first dropping abruptly, the Moon Bug leveled out into a shallow glide over the plain.

"Altitude 50 feet," Kovac said. "Hope that dark slash you talk about isn't a ridge."

"If it is, it's low. We'll lift her over." Squinting, he peered through the lower port, silently cursing the exhaust glare. Suddenly he saw something that jerked him to attention. "Movement," he gasped. "I see movement!"

"Movement!" The incredulous word came over the radio.

"The patch is moving, a welling movement . . . sort of a tidal swell. Oh, oh, here it comes!" He drew his head back instinctively, his brain racing for answers.

"What is it?" He didn't answer and seconds later the voice came, more frantically this time. "Moon Bug! Moon Bug!" It sounded as if both Burke and Mallon were on at the same time.

"Below 2 percent fuel," Kovac rasped tightly.

"It's ash," Faulk exclaimed, regaining his voice. "Ash whipped up by the exhaust blast. It doesn't float . . . there's no air . . . but it comes in ballistic trajectories. It's covering the ports—"

"Watch that black slash," Mallon cut in. "Could be a ridge."

"Can't see it . . . blinded."

"You'd better lift her."

"Not enough fuel. Like riding in a sandstorm at midnight."

"How deep?" Burke broke in.

"The ash? Can't tell. Can't see a thing. Completely blinding. We'll try to cross to the other edge."

"Might be rock outcrops—"

"Little over 1 percent fuel," Kovac rasped.

"I'll watch it. I've got the beam on in that direction but can't see beyond the ash curtain. It's fine, fine flakes, moves in a jillion trajectories. Like a snowstorm. Oh, oh, Max is having trouble with the altimeter readings. The ash. But we're around fifty feet. Now . . . I can see the border. Ash thinning. Using the beam. Rock, twisted rocks . . . jutting high. Can't get out that way. I'll follow the border." His hands flashed to the controls and triggered two keys

—one gimbaled a jet, the other fired it. In quick succession he fired several others. The Bug lurched into a new course.

"Set down at the first clear spot," Burke said tautly.

"Can't see any. Just rocks . . . gnarled and sprawling, not real high but high enough to smash us. Can't get over 'em. Following border."

"One percent fuel," Kovac cut in.

"I'm going to set down . . . see if I can find a balance between rock and ash." He punched a button. A servo mechanism started a small electric motor and a tubular metal framework extended outward, forming four ungainly legs ending in elephant-foot touchdown pads. The one he glimpsed through the lower port resembled a pillow on a crab leg. "Landing gear extended."

"Don't wipe it out."

"Try not. Still at the edge of the ash. It's coming up . . . bad. Rugged rocks to the other side. I'm reversing course, going down about ten feet . . . will try to sweep an area clean, see how deep the ash is . . . what's under it." He gimbaled and fired the jets again, at the same time changing throttle. The Moon Bug went into a pitch attitude and he corrected it, adjusting with four or five jets until it was moving back along its course, at the same time dropping.

"Fuel at one-half percent," Kovac said, without moving his eyes from the instruments.

"Altitude?"

"Should be around 20 . . . 20 above the pads. Sink rate indicator acting up." The copilot spoke in a jerky voice.

"Guess altitude 20 feet," Faulk snapped tersely. "Going down to guess 10. Ash is terrible. Can't see the rocky border. Nothing. I've swung the beam straight down . . . blinding but I've got to see. Can't depend on instruments. Ash is swirling like a tremendous sandstorm. Oh, oh, some black . . . some black through the ash.

I've gimbaled the jets . . . giving 'em full power to hold us up a bit."

"Zero percent fuel," Kovac rapped out edgily.

"Max says zero on the fuel. Still going down. Trying to hold steady but can't. Slipping into pitch. Ash looks deep, deep, but the exhaust is boring through. Rocks right next to us, jagged and— Oh, there she goes . . . main engines off. Small jets can't . . . We're falling . . ."

Chapter 10

Wuuuump! A grinding, crunching rumble came from underfoot followed by a violent shock that slammed Faulk against the seat-pan, knocking the wind from his lungs. *This was it!* It flooded his mind as the Moon Bug tottered, leaning precariously before it came to rest. He sat for several seconds before the realization came. They were down—alive! He cast a fast look around, not believing the cabin could be intact.

In the intense silence that followed, Kovac exclaimed, "Made it!" They stared incredulously at each other. Faulk drew a deep breath and exhaled slowly.

"Max," he said, "we made it." He laughed, a quiet laugh of self-satisfaction.

"Came in on a prayer," the copilot said, his voice frank with wonder. His eyes darted to the instrument panel. "Cabin pressure steady . . . steady at four point two." He switched to the inclinometer. "Canted . . . close to ten degrees."

"Hit hard . . ." Bleeding the air from his suit, Faulk opened his faceplate, finishing: "Hope we didn't damage the engines."

"Yeah." They exchanged a rapid glance.

Faulk became aware of Mallon's worried call on the radio and acknowledged, adding, "Bug landed at T plus 64 minutes from start of go-down."

"Congratulations, Skipper. You had us sweating." Mallon's voice displayed his relief.

"Had *us* sweating, you mean." Faulk laughed again, unable to contain his jubilance. "Practically an instrument landing, Les."

"Whaddya know?" the other said admiringly.

"Any damage?" The voice, faint and worried, was Burke's.

"Hi, Whitey, we made it. Can't tell yet. We slammed down pretty hard. Hope the landing gear absorbed most of it. Cabin's pressure-tight but we're canted about ten degrees."

"Feel steady . . . safe?"

"Believe so. We'll know better when we see the landing structure."

"You were fairly low," Burke encouraged.

"A few feet."

"How about the ash—are you in it?"

"Don't know. Felt like we hit solid rock. I'm bruised where I sit."

"Hold it while I flash the word," Burke exclaimed. "Everyone's waiting. We have an open line to the White House. The NASA brass—" Abruptly he broke off.

"Big commotion," Kovac commented. "Someone must have done sumpin'."

"Wonder who?" They looked at each other and grinned.

"Feel like a hero already," Kovac said. His face took on a sober expression. "I dread all the malarky when we get home."

"I'll fill in for you," Mallon cut in.

"You'll be there anyway."

"Sure, I love parades. The Lone Space Ranger, that's me. The kids will eat it up. Chapter One: Alone Around the Moon. How's that for an opener?"

"Some people are born to clown," Kovac remarked.

"A form of art."

They exchanged banter until Burke came back on. He spoke quickly: "I've flashed the word. The Nation will be wild. Karen and Eve say the TV people have been around all day . . . stringing wire and rolling up lights. They're going to be on a national network. You should see their letters and telegrams—by the ton."

"Look—" Faulk started to protest when Burke cut him short.

"Forget it, Joe. You're a celebrity. You all are. This is part of it. Besides, they'll love it. It's not for them; it's for you and Max. You'll have to get used to it. You're a trio of famous guys."

"Who's been handing you that smoke, Whitey?"

"Clayborn."

"Who?"

"Oscar Clayborn, a press agent type. They brought him in to do you justice, build up your public image. Man, you should see the stuff he's handing out! Remember the line: *Oh, give me a ship, a tall, tall ship, and a star to steer her by?* He's got that on a release he's giving out now. Then he says: *Today Pilot-Captain Joseph Faulk, commanding the NASA Spaceship Apollo, followed that star and landed on the Moon.* That's class, Joe."

"The Moon Bug," he objected, thinking Burke couldn't be serious. "Not Apollo."

"He's good," Burke asserted, as if he hadn't heard. "He's the guy who made Marie Margo's legs famous."

"Good Lord!" Faulk exploded.

"Great stuff," Mallon broke in. "Slip him a few words about me —the intrepid navigator, alone in the gulfs of space, pointing the path for future man. He ought to really go for that."

"But what's it like?" Burke broke in. "The whole world is waiting to know." His voice rose eagerly. "What's it like, Joe?"

"Like?" Faulk leaned toward the blurred port, peering, and groped for words to describe what met his eyes. "A shadowland, Whitey, dusky with earthlight, splotched with black—big gobs of it.

We're next to a low ridge of jagged rock—at least it throws a jagged shadow. I see small clefts with bottoms that resemble ash-covered paths. It's tangled, wild."

"Craters . . . gulfs?"

"Can't really tell, but I don't think so. Not craters, but some of the shadows look like rifts. Ever see the slope of Mauna Loa? Twist the rock and throw in the moonlight and it'd look like that."

"We're taping this for rebroadcast, Joe. Don't miss anything. How about the patch?"

Faulk swung to the side port. "Like a formless plain," he said, "like desert sands under a yellow moon, but less bright . . . or maybe it's the glass. It's a weird place, Whitey, like nothing you ever saw. You almost expect to see coyotes, rabbits, sage. No, it's even too barren for that. Did you ever fly low over Death Valley? It's like that, but bleaker. That slash we saw . . . it is a crevice."

"A wide one," Kovac interrupted. "If we'd landed there, we'd be talking to you from the center of the moon. It's deep, something you know without knowing. It'll give us a view of the subsurface rocks. But Joe's right, you can't see a thing in the shadows. It's eerie."

Faulk switched on the search beam. The black shadows in its path dissolved, leaving gaunt, dark rocks that protruded above the patch in weird skeletal forms. "It shows a sheen under the light . . . like obsidian or volcanic glass," he conjectured.

"The press is yammering for the first description."

"Wild, tangled, desolate," he responded. "And beautiful."

"It's a wild, tangled, desolate and beautiful surface," Burke yelled aside to someone, and then into the mike: "I have a pile of congratulatory messages."

"Already prepared, huh?"

Burke laughed. "We knew you'd do it. You've just edged Columbus out of the number one slot."

"Save the congrats," Faulk answered. "Tell Karen and Eve."

"They knew the instant Les contacted you, Joe. They're in seventh heaven."

"Thanks," he said, relieved. "We'll get set up. I want to get out and look over the engine structure."

"We'll be standing by."

"Standing by," Mallon echoed. "I'll try to relay through the satellite when I'm over the hump. We have a fair track on it. If you can't get me—"

"We won't worry," Faulk cut in. "We'll be in contact with Whitey."

"Roger, Skipper."

While Kovac read a detailed report of operational data and events into a recorder for automatic transmission to earth, Faulk checked the portable life support equipment they would use on the moon. Despite his impatience, he forced himself to go slowly over each item, giving special attention to the valves regulating oxygen pressure and small thermal controls. Finished, they inflated their suits, vented the cabin air and opened the hatch, peering out silently, drinking in the strangeness confronting them. With the blurriness of the glass removed, the dark patches were limned in sharp detail, the areas lighted by earthshine brighter. Deadly still and spectral, it held a ghost-haunted quality that sent a slight shiver down Faulk's spine. Devoid of pattern, it was a world that could have been slapped together on a dark night.

"Fantastic," Kovac murmured.

"A nightmare." Their eyes met. "It's going to be interesting, Max."

"Yeah." The copilot scanned the ashy surface under them.

The operational plan called for one man to stay with the ship while the other explored, gathering specimens and radioing his findings to the cabin, where they would be recorded for transmission to earth. The moment had come.

"Go down," Faulk urged. "Touch the moon, Max."

"It's your honor, Joe."

"Nuts, I have glory enough. Touch it, Max, then I'll explore."

"No, Skipper . . ."

Faulk watched his eyes, heard his words tinkle in the phones. His voice was grave, solemn, caught with the momentousness of this instant in history. *The first human foot, the first other world.* . . . The man who first touched the moon would capture history. . . . The simple act of taking the final step down would ensure that. Voice and face reflected his wonder even as he rejected the opportunity. But he'd earned it, Faulk mused. He'd been a rock.

"We're both in history," he said quietly. "So's Les, so go ahead. Touch it, Max."

"Okay . . . okay, Joe." Kovac drew a deep breath and threw down a rope ladder. As he prepared to descend, Faulk got a long, tubular container and lowered it alongside the ladder with a piece of cord. Kovac stepped down slowly. His body swayed from side to side and he had difficulty, hampered by the heavy gloves and cumbersome suit and backpack. Midway he paused, studying the Bug's underside.

"Engines look okay," he reported. "The legs and crushable bumper are pretty well mangled but they did the work. One corner is caved in more than the others—"

"Look steady?" Faulk interrupted.

"I'd say so. We could have trouble during launch."

"We'll check it." He sensed the sudden relief of ridding himself of a nagging worry.

When Kovac reached the bottom rung, he paused to look up before deliberately pressing his boot against the ash. Instead of stepping down, he withdrew his foot, bewitched by the mark he'd made.

"Look, Joe"—he turned his face upward—"first human footstep on the moon. I feel like Robinson Crusoe when he found the footstep in the sand."

"Except that this is your footstep, Max. The first."

"The first," Kovac echoed, his voice muffled with emotion. He stood erect, gazing around, surveying the world he had inherited. For a brief moment he held the pose, then got the tubular case Faulk had lowered and opening it, withdrew a collapsible rod. Extending it to full length, he rotated it to unfurl the American flag. Probing the ash, he lodged the rod in a crevice. Finished, he stepped back, looking at it before awkwardly saluting. Faulk, who had followed suit, felt a lump in his throat.

"Wait." He turned to the radio, and when Burke acknowledged, announced, "Today on 8 July 1969, at 11:10 P.M., Eastern Standard Time, Major Max Kovac, United States Air Force, pressed his foot against the moon. His first words were: *First human footstep on the moon.*

"Six words for history," Burke proclaimed. "They'll make world headlines."

"His first act was to plant the American flag," he continued. "It flies there now . . . in the lunar night."

"Wonderful, wonderful, Joe."

"Call you back. Gotta help Max."

"Roger," Burke acknowledged. "I'll pass the word."

Returning to the hatch, Faulk looked down. "Now you can go to work. I'll lower the gear."

"Work—such a famous man?"

"Stand by or I'll drop it on you."

Faulk lowered a folding portable antenna which used a light-seeking servo system to track earth. Erected, it would serve a UHF transceiver that provided voice and telemetry exchange between the Moon Bug and earth, and standard FM transmission used to communicate with Apollo. With the mast up, Burke's voice came through loud and clear. Not till then did Faulk realize how weak their communications had been. Kovac reported the temperature at minus 236 degrees Fahrenheit and no measurable atmosphere.

"But there might be some, Joe—deep, at the bottoms of craters or crevices," he insisted. He climbed clumsily back to the cabin. "Go down, try it," he urged. "It's wonderful."

"How's the suit?"

"Cumbersome but you'll be surprised how easy it is to move—next thing to being weightless. Temp controls are good."

Faulk inspected the small hand tools and specimen containers hooked to his belt, and turned toward the hatch. "Here I go, second man on the moon." He moved his foot to the top rung of the ladder, cautiously stepping down. His body swayed and he had trouble controlling his movements until he got the hang of it. Reaching the bottom, he stepped briskly to the moon. Throwing a beam on the engine housing, he inspected it critically, then noted the buckled legs and calculated their ability to support the Bug during the few seconds of engine firing required to build sufficient thrust to lift clear.

"Looks okay," he finally announced. "I'll explore the rocks. Tape me."

"Keep in line of sight," Kovac cautioned.

"Will do."

He flashed the beam over the low ridge, skirting the edge for an opening. At first the low lunar gravity, one-sixth that of earth, made walking and balance difficult. The energy imparted into a normal step threw him forward several feet. Once he learned to control his muscles he increased his pace; with adeptness came comfort and ease. As Kovac said, walking was like floating. He reached a cleft in the ridge and tapped the rock with a small hammer.

"Chips like glass," he reported.

He put a specimen in the container, studying his surroundings. The rock outcrops were low, coarse, craggy. Rising out of the ground in distorted shapes, some reached upward like beseeching fingers, others sprawled across the dusty floor, reminding him of serpents slithering over a sandy wasteland. A fine mantle of dust lay over their black tops and flat surfaces, filling pores and crevices. Dust of ten million years, he mused. He looked back at the boot marks scuffed in the ash. They, too, would be there for ten million years. Or would they vanish under cities? Most of the rock was black, but occasionally he saw grays and tans, a few white streaks resembling quartz.

Reporting his findings, he moved carefully, conscious that a ripped suit meant death. A view from atop an obsidian spur revealed an ebon expanse daubed with cream—or was it the other way around? From his vantage point, the Ocean of Storms looked flat. Earthlight reflected from it as a deep citron color, giving far less illumination than predicted. He saw gross forms rather than detail. Oceanus Procellarum stretched monotonously toward the horizon. *Is this the moon? Is it all like this?* No, for there were craters, vast mountain ranges, strange radiating lines and terraces that held color; he had seen them from orbit and during descent. But now they were far away. From orbit the Ocean of Storms appeared flat; from here it was broken, rough, drear. Procellarum— the great wasteland of the moon. Would it be different had he landed on Mare Imbrium? he wondered.

"Les due overhead," Kovac reported. "He'll come over the local horizon in five minutes."

"Plug me in." He turned, looking back along his path.

The Bug had come to rest perilously near the rock rim; to the other side lay the sweep of the patch, broken by a vast crevice. In the dim earthshine the vehicle resembled a big-bodied spider crouched at the edge of the dusty plain, distinguishable from the bordering rocks only by its symmetry. Clearly it was alien to its surroundings, the handiwork of an other-world artificer. Yet it seemed part of the bleak land on which it stood, as ancient as the gnarled rock. Despite crushed legs and canted body, it clearly was a ship structured to cross the void. He let his eyes wander toward the horizon. Earthshine, dust and black rock—the pattern was sameness.

"Apollo above local lunar horizon." The copilot spoke crisply. "He'll flash a beam when he's ninety degrees overhead."

"Give me an alert."

"Will do. Les says it's nice being alone—gives him time to dwell on the finer things of life."

"Girls?"

"What else?" Kovac asked.

Faulk moved on slowly. The ash—or was it dust?—was never deep, seldom more than a half-inch or so. But here and there he encountered deep potholes, as if the surface had been gouged randomly. *Meteors,* he reflected. *Big meteors.* He wondered how many ages had passed since the fury had struck. Cutting across the patch, he reached the edge of the chasm. Wider than he had supposed—around fifteen or twenty feet, he judged—it lay like a slash across the citron-colored surface. Turning the beam downward, he studied the rock walls, then leaned cautiously over the edge trying to see bottom. The light bounced off the walls, dying in the darkness. The abyss seemed bottomless.

Making a mental note to explore it later, he was heading back to the Moon Bug when Kovac cut in: "Apollo 10 seconds to local zenith."

"Roger." He paused, scanning the sky above. Ten thousand stars glowed, some in colors never seen from earth. The Pleiades blazed a cold ice-blue from the heart of Taurus. Canopus burned with a furious yellow-white light; over there was orange Aldebaran. His eyes riveted directly overhead, he caught a tiny light moving among the stars at the same instant Kovac's voice came through the phones:

"Mark."

"Mark," he replied. A few seconds later the light blinked out.

"We've established the instant the Apollo rises above the local horizon and time from local horizon to zenith," the copilot informed him. "The rendezvous maneuver could be as easy as falling off a log."

"We hope," he responded, knowing that it simply wasn't true.

Coming down they had but to hit a world; going up they would have to find a spaceship that in the void would be as a grain of sand to a desert. Max knew that, he reflected. Still, he felt heartened at the copilot's confidence. In truth, he felt the same. The feat of safely landing the Moon Bug under the almost impossible conditions had given him a tremendous surge of confidence. He chipped small slivers of the gray and tan rocks and scooped up a handful of ash for the specimen containers, then gazed around. What else? Nothing else. The Ocean of Storm was a world of sameness, a Sahara placed on the moon. Those were the tangible attributes. The intangible one was solitude, and his reaction to it—loneliness. In all the universe, could there be a more bleak spot? He doubted it. When he reached the Bug, Max was eagerly waiting to go.

"I'm going to sample the patch, take a gander at the crevice," Max informed him.

"Careful," Faulk warned.

"Don't worry." Kovac smiled reassuringly. "I'm not about to goof."

"Don't," he admonished. He watched Kovac descend, then turned to the radio and chatted with Burke and Mallon. The latter was describing an autobiography he was going to write—*The Intrepid Navigator*—when he suddenly broke off with a sharp exclamation.

"Apollo, Apollo . . ." Faulk spoke urgently into the phones, hearing Burke repeat the call. He felt a quick alarm.

Mallon came back on, saying crisply, "Got a red light and alarm bell on the meteorite impact indicator," he explained. "Cabin pressure's steady. Must have been small."

"Keep your eye on the gauge," Burke warned. "You might have a small leak that'll sneak up on you."

"Will do. I'm keeping my suit pressurized till I know," Mallon answered. "Gives me a shaky feeling."

"The intrepid navigator," Burke snorted.

"I've just put you on my list."

"Okay, okay, you're a hero," Faulk cut in. "Just watch the gauge."

Mallon was making a hurt reply when Kovac came on: "There are a few small rock outcrops, a little roughness, but the patch is fairly flat. The ash is thin—less than half an inch. I'm standing in the swath cleared by our exhaust."

"Saw it," Faulk replied. "It sure looked deeper."

"The floor's a clay color . . . about the same as the ash. We just couldn't make it out."

"Could have made a perfect touchdown," he groaned.

"We didn't know, Joe."

"This quarter-earth illumination . . . like flying blind."

"Next to no light at all," Kovac agreed. "I'm going to look at the crevice." A few moments later his voice came on again. "It's wide, twenty or so feet in places, as if it had been torn open by a quake. The beam doesn't show much except it's jagged."

"I saw it, Max."

"Beat me, huh. Could you see bottom?"

"The outcrops shadowed it," he explained.

After a brief silence, Kovac said, "From the slope of the walls, I'd say it must be a hundred feet or more deep."

"All of that," he agreed.

They discussed it for a while, then Kovac began circling the perimeter of the patch to gather specimens. Waiting, Faulk reflected that for a lifetime he'd dreamed of such an adventure as this. Go-down had been a bear; go-up and rendezvous could be even tougher. But the moon itself excited and stimulated him. True, it didn't look particularly hazardous at the moment, or at least the small sample he'd had of it, but this was just the dawn. The suits were safe, temperature controls were good, and meteoroid fall didn't appear to offer any great hazard. Yet the scape was alien, hostile—threatening in ways he sensed but couldn't identify. There were mysteries here, secrets, problems that would occupy the human mind for generations. Perhaps, in time, there would be domed cities, underground dwellings, spaceports—terminals with such signs as *Ramp 3 for Mars Express, Ramp 4 for* . . . He smiled at the picture. But it was true; man was just at the beginning of a tremendous outward expansion.

He gazed through the port, feeling again the strangeness. He was the first, but he was but a unit in a vast system—an agent in a plan so complicated as to be almost incomprehensible. Schools, laboratories, scores of scientific disciplines and hundreds of sprawling industries had combined to land one small vehicle on a barren moon patch. Years of dreams, blueprints, tests, prototype hardware, and now he was here. And Max. And up there was Les. Every two hours Apollo swept overhead, monitoring the doings on the patch, preparing for the Bug's ascent, sending data to men and machines over 240,000 miles away. Contemplating it, he felt humble.

He was surprised and pleased when Phil Herndon came on for a short chat. The Government was delighted; the Nation was in the throes of a tumultuous celebration; Max, Les and himself were the heroes of the day—that was the essence of his words.

"Senator Halpern is the only objector," he added.

"Still unhappy?"

"He wants to know what we got for our money—dollars and cents."

"We got a world, Phil."

"Sure, but he has an answer for that." Faulk waited—nothing would surprise him. "What has it produced? That's his question. Just goes to show you." They talked for a while longer. Before signing off, Herndon revealed that a big push was being generated for follow-on flights. More, it was coming from the general public. Even the staid *New York Times* had referred to earth's satellite as the fifty-first state.

When Kovac returned, they set up the portable television on the patch to transmit pictures to Apollo for relay to earth. The first shot showed the American flag. They shot scenes without lights showing the Bug's dark profile silhouetted in earthshine, the vehicle bathed in light, the black rocks and plain—Kovac crossing a field of ash.

Burke was ecstatic. "Magnificent!" he exclaimed. "Like a Hollywood production. We're rebroadcasting it to the world."

"Should have shaved," Kovac complained. "This shoots the image of the astronaut as a clean-scrubbed American boy."

"Max, the gals will love you," Burke promised. "You'll replace Les as the feminine dream."

"Never," Mallon cut in. "In the final analysis, it's a matter of charm."

Following the banter came five magical minutes during which Faulk spoke with Karen across the gulf separating two worlds.

"I'll be back . . . soon," he promised, as their time came to an end.

"Hurry, honey," she urged.

Afterward, Kovac spoke with Eve. Finished, he quietly regarded Faulk.

"That alone makes it worth it," he said.

"Yes, it does." Faulk knew exactly how he felt.

During the two following orbits they worked with Mallon and Cap. Com to establish the exact times, thrust, and flight profile they would use during go-up and rendezvous. They confirmed the exact instant Apollo rose above the local horizon, the exact instant it passed ninety degrees overhead, the exact instant Faulk would fire the main engines, lifting the Bug from the lunar surface.

Azimuth and vehicle attitudes were refined, with the final figures worked out on the NASA computers and flashed back across the void. The machines gave the answers in mathematics, plotted curves that made everything appear quite simple. But it wasn't simple, Faulk mused. Computers, man-made geniuses, took everything into account—except the human himself. Intelligence, emotion, reaction, human decision-making and human error—these were factors alien to the machines, and because they were, the machines disregarded them.

No, it wouldn't be simple.

"I'd like to take another look at the crevice," Kovac said as their time on the moon drew near end. "It would be interesting to know if the rock structure changes with depth."

He adjusted his backpack and looped a coil of rope over his shoulder. Faulk eyed the line thoughtfully.

"Careful," he warned.

"There are plenty of foot- and handholds," Kovac replied. "I'll watch it, Joe." Testing his flashlight, he adjusted his backpack and turned toward the ladder.

"Take it easy," Faulk cautioned again.

"Will do."

Kovac slowly descended the ladder, pausing at the bottom to look at the flag. Transferred to the top of the high antenna, it offered the only bit of color on an otherwise bleak and murky world. Crossing the patch, his boots kicked up small spurts of dust. The hardpan was uneven and he moved carefully, fearful of stepping into a pothole. The patch stretched before him, a dusky sulphur-yellow backdropped by low, rimming rocks that cut uneven notches in the sky. Above gleamed the stars.

Reaching the crevice, he peered down into the blackness for a long moment before turning on the flashlight. Splashing over the rocks, its beams showed a startling silver in the dusk. In whatever fashion the gulf had been created, its sides were left splintered and rough, with innumerable rock outcrops that offered handholds and foot rests. Turning the light toward the bottom, his eyes followed the beam; light clay-colored layers of rock undershot with black extended as far down as he could see.

"At the edge of the crevice," he reported. "I'm going down."

"Watch it, Max."

"I'll loop a rope over a rocky knob. No sweat. There are plenty of handholds. I'll be out of radio contact for a while."

"Ten minutes," Faulk said firmly.

"Make it twenty."

"No longer, Max."

"Roger. Don't worry."

Securing the rope, he gripped the flashlight firmly and let himself down over the edge, testing until he found a jutting rock. He took a second step, and a third. With the rope looped under his arms in mountaineer fashion, he leaned back, letting it out slowly, then began descending with more confidence. Slowly the chasm walls rose above him, closing out all but a thin slash of the starfield. Occasionally the rock, glinting under the light, displayed evidences of crystalline formation and he paused to chip small specimens, dropping them into a container. Before he realized, he came to the end of the line. Feet braced against the walls, he looked down.

Bottom! He could see it, a scant twenty or so feet below. Instead of closing together in a V, it looked several feet wide with an ash-sprinkled bottom. His eyes calculated the walls below him. Nearly vertical, they nevertheless were studded with solid outcrops. His muscles felt stiff and unresponsive and it came to him he was cold. Pausing, he adjusted the heating elements in his suit. Relinquishing his grip on the line, he gingerly took a step downward, his hands gripping the rock. The flashlight proved disturbing and reluctantly he turned it off, letting it dangle from his belt. In the absolute blackness he groped for handholds, moving downward inch by inch until finally, his foot found a flatness. He moved the other foot down alongside it, testing until he knew he'd reached bottom. Sighing with relief, he let go with one hand, fumbled for the light and turned it on.

Splaying off the sides of the narrow chasm, its sharp beams momentarily blinded him and he waited without moving until his eyes began to adapt. The walls rose above him, sheer and black, and far up he saw a thin slash of stars. Here and there he perceived small splashes of gray and the occasional sparkle of what appeared to be crystalline or metallic substances. He studied the walls carefully, playing the light into small cracks while he examined them for specimens. Suddenly he paused, holding very still. *Not rock, not rock . . .* The phrase ran through his mind.

Bending eagerly forward, he ran his fingers along the edge of a fissure.

Faulk looked up from the radio, vaguely uncomfortable. Twenty-two minutes. He should be hearing from Max. When thirty minutes had passed, he grew worried. Apprising Burke of the situation, he moved to the edge of the hatch, staring toward the chasm. It lay like a ghostly black ribbon in the earthshine.

"Max!" he called peremptorily several times, even though he knew it to be futile, but just the act of trying to contact him tended to relieve his anxiety. "Max!" His voice rang hollow in his ears. If Kovac didn't return in another five minutes, he'd alert Burke, go to the crevice. He was fuming over it when his phones crackled.

"Joe!"

"What is it?" he demanded, alarmed. Staring out, he saw movement at the edge of the plain.

"A minute," Kovac gasped.

"Max?"

"A minute," he repeated. Kovac ran awkwardly toward him across the ash. Faulk waited, suppressing his worry. Kovac reached the ladder and began scrambling up. Breathing heavily at the top, he pulled himself into the cabin, thrusting a specimen container toward Faulk.

"Life," he gasped. "Life."

"Slow down."

"It's life, I tell you—small, microscopic, but it's a life form."

"What?" Faulk felt a quick excitement.

"Here." He shook the container. "Perhaps there's a residual atmosphere deep in the craters . . . or maybe it's a life that's adapted, learned to extract oxygen from rock."

"Are you positive, Max? Positive it's organic?"

"I'm positive." Kovac paused, catching his breath. "There's no mistake, Joe. It's like a lichen, perhaps a semimetallic form, but it's life. That much I know."

"Life," Faulk echoed wonderingly.

"Do you know what this means, Joe? It means we're not alone. Not alone, I tell you." He stepped to the hatch and flung an arm toward the firmament. "There's life out there, Joe. Life."

Chapter 11

"Your NBC announcer Martin Lorry, bringing you the latest news of our men on the moon." Lorry smiled crisply into the camera, cocking his head in a gesture familiar to millions. "Just a few moments ago NASA revealed that the astronauts are preparing to launch upward from their lunar base . . . make rendezvous with Apollo. To give you the background of that story, we have with us a familiar guest—Mr. Philip Herndon of the National Aeronautics and Space Administration. Mr. Herndon."

The camera swung to Herndon's face. Eyes deeply buried under heavy orbital ridges, lines of strain and a new heaviness around the jowls gave it a haggard look. Light shone on the scalp where the gray hair had thinned.

"Mr. Herndon, what is the situation on the moon right now?"

"As you know, one of the astronauts . . . Les Mallon . . . is orbiting the moon in the Apollo. The other two, Joe Faulk and Max Kovac, are on the moon. They landed, of course, with the Lunar Excursion Module."

"The Moon Bug?"

"It's popularly called that, yes. It's small of course, just large enough for two men and the equipment needed to sustain life during the trip and on the moon." He chuckled. "Not exactly pullman accommodations. It's quite crowded with gear, of course—life support, the equipment needed on the moon."

"Sort of a space-going motorcycle," Lorry suggested.

"A miniature spaceship." He nodded. "It has separate go-up and go-down engines and two tank systems—one for descent and one for ascent."

"Does that include fuel used by the small jets?"

"Reaction control jets? No. The fuel there is tanked separately— a completely independent system."

"I understand the empty tank—the descent tank—is jettisoned during upward launch."

"That is right, and so are the landing gear and descent engines."

"Then launch is a pretty stripped-down affair?"

"You could say that." Herndon smiled slightly. "We haven't room for the extras."

"How much fuel does the Moon Bug carry, Mr. Herndon?"

"Enough to accomplish its mission—rendezvous."

"But no extra?"

"No, there are weight considerations."

"How will the Moon Bug contact Apollo, Mr. Herndon?"

"I'm not sure that I understand the question."

"I'm talking about radar . . . things like that."

"Yes, they use radar. They will also have radio, visual sightings and, of course, computational data. The latter is really the most important—knowing precise launch azimuth, time, engine firing and things like that. I might add that these are worked out here, by NASA computers from data supplied by Apollo and radioed back."

"To Apollo?"

"And the Moon Bug."

"You mentioned visual sightings . . . ?"

"Yes, at least in the final stages."

"Then Joe Faulk, on the moon, will actually be able to see Apollo. Is that right, Mr. Herndon?"

"During final closure, yes, and perhaps for quite some time before that. However, actual lock-on will be achieved by radar."

"So if one system fails . . . ?"

"The others serve as backup," Herndon supplied.

"It sounds somewhat like a jet fighter operation."

"Yes."

"I understand they're having some trouble with the glass—that this is sort of a blind-flying feat."

"Not true," Herndon replied shortly. "At least it's a great exaggeration. There has been some erosion of the ports, probably due to encounter with high-velocity dust particles."

"On both vehicles?"

"Yes, but we don't consider it dangerous. Not yet."

"Tell me, Mr. Herndon, is this a dangerous operation?"

"I don't know what you mean by dangerous, Mr. Lorry, but it's certainly a ticklish one. It's a split-second operation, if that's what you mean."

"So if anything goes wrong . . . ?"

"In that case there is a real danger, yes."

"What is the greatest danger, Mr. Herndon?"

"I really couldn't say." The faint smile returned again. "After all, this is the first time."

"I can see that," Lorry agreed. "Well, this has been very informative, Mr. Herndon, and we're very happy to have had you with us today." They shook hands briefly and the camera focused on the announcer's face again.

"Now I'd like to give you a fast rundown of comments received in street corner interviews across the nation:

"A Seattle doctor: *This proves man isn't limited to earth.*

"A New York stockbroker: *Aerospace issues should do very well.*

"A Dallas industrialist: *It'll probably wind up as a United Nations issue.*

"A Kansas City educator: *This vindicates our emphasis on the sciences.*

"A San Diego housewife: *The moon? It sounds awfully far away.*"

Martin Lorry ceased speaking, looked at the audience and smiled.

"Now for a word from our sponsor . . ."

Go-up.

T minus 20 minutes to launch.

Adjusting the pilot's seat and harnessing, Faulk reviewed the preparations for blast-off, mentally checking each item of the complex list, at the same time conscious of an odd sorrow. Because he was leaving the moon? No, his job was done, or would be once he completed rendezvous. In a narrow sense, the important thing was to "prove the system"—show that a lunar landing and takeoff was practical. The overall goal—"The political goal," as Herndon called it—was to win the lunar sweepstakes. That had been done.

Suddenly he realized he was tired, very tired. The exhilaration and eagerness were gone, leaving in their wake a curious numbness which pervaded mind and body. His hands performed their tasks automatically, responding to training and experience as if they were instruments apart from his mind. And that was dangerous! Kovac must feel the same, and Mallon. Three tired men. He made a concerted effort to focus his mind on the immediate, and on go-up—plan ahead.

"Faceplates," Kovac said, scanning his countdown list.

Faulk absently closed his mask and bled pressure into the suit, feeling it grow into a rigid constrictive wall around his body. His hands took on a heavy, numb sensation. Well, they'd won the lunar sweepstakes, he reflected. The flag atop the antenna attested to that. Time to return. Still he sensed a reluctance. He knew so little of the moon—one small patch of ash on the bosom of a rocky sea. He adjusted a temperature control. He'd better forget that now. This was the critical hour, the critical operation. Stripped to its ultimate meaning, it was life or death.

Finished with his gear, he asked, "Cabin pressure?"

"Steady at 4.2," Kovac replied tautly.

Glancing at him, all Faulk saw were the intent dark eyes, bushy brows, a few patches of olive skin. The rest was helmet. A gloved hand rested on the edge of the instrument console.

"We'd better dark adapt," Faulk said.

"Roger."

Kovac flicked a master switch extinguishing all light except that of the small red lamps illuminating the instruments and controls. His faceplate acquired a reddish sheen, masking his dark eyes and bushy brows. He focused a red beam on the countdown sheet, peering at it. Faulk blinked to adjust his vision.

Launch time was based on the passage of Apollo through the dark vault overhead. It had been checked by radar, timer, optical angle. Verified by stellar fixes and information from both Apollo and earth, the data had been fed into the guidance computer. Go-up was almost the reverse of go-down except for differences in power usage and attitude. The go-up engines would carry them to pericynthion at 50,000 feet—drive them to the tremendous speed they would need to carry them halfway around the moon while slowly spiraling outward toward orbital altitude. Reaction jets would provide additional power for added velocity and maneuver. His eyes scanned the board. Operational systems had been energized. Communication systems had been checked and life support systems tested. Every facet of flight readiness had been combed. This was Kovac's job. Watching him—the alert voice and quick responses—Faulk again felt thankful at his choice. Kovac must be as tired and numb as he, yet somehow, he seemed to reach into a reserve reservoir of energy and bring it into play. He couldn't do better than Max, he mused, watching the clock. His own time would begin at T minus zero. The critical hour.

While following the quick exchanges between the copilot and Burke, he rehearsed his own role—"The trial by fire," as Phil Herndon put it. He knew exactly what he had to do, the exact time to do it. Every action, every second, existed as a plan of action imprinted on his brain. He would do this and this and that. In that respect, he was little more than an automaton. Except for the unpredictables! That was the catch, the reason for his being here. Machines were more accurate, more reliable, but they lacked judgment—the ability to make snap decisions in the face of emergency. Machines couldn't cope with the unexpected. They were creatures of response—laborers who toiled in the vineyards of a programed world. But space was the realm of the unpredictable; he'd had that drilled into him since his earliest days with the astronauts.

He tried to anticipate possible emergencies, gearing his response to each. The Bug's leg assembly was designed to form a launching pad that remained on the moon as the vehicle lifted. But supposing the legs hung up . . . didn't break free? Supposing the ascent engines had been damaged? Supposing . . .

"Apollo will reach horizon in sixty seconds," Burke said, breaking the silence. "I'll give you a time hack."

Faulk brought back his attention, surprised at the quick passage of time. Kovac moved a hand to one of the timers, now at zero. At fifty-five seconds, Burke picked up the count: ". . . 56, 57, 58, 59 . . . mark!"

"Mark!" Kovac punched a button to start the timer at the same instant Mallon's voice came through:

"Mark—Apollo above lunar horizon."

"Roger, we have you on timer."

"Are you flight ready?"

"At go," Kovac said flatly.

Faulk followed the exchange, a routine he knew by heart. He had gone through it a thousand times—in classrooms, in mockup simulators, even in his dreams. But this was the first live firing of the Bug in an operational launch from a non-earth surface, and he followed it with interest. No room for error.

Optical angle is . . .

Radar range is . . .

Time is . . .

The information flowed back and forth between two worlds and between a space vehicle on one of the worlds and another circling high above it. *Range rate is . . .* Faulk flicked his eyes to the patch. A single gaunt antenna rose above the ash, topped by the American flag. Alongside was a small portable television camera and transmitter which, starting automatically at time zero, would record the Bug's engine firing and lift-off and transmit the pictures to Apollo for relay to earth. It was strange to see them there, products of a technical civilization adorning the desert of a world which had never known life save, perhaps, microscopic cells that dwelt deep in the moon chasms. Perhaps in some distant time chance travelers would stumble across the antenna and TV—prize them as relics from man's dim past. Scientists would ponder their origin.

"I read you at T plus 5 minutes to launch," said Mallon.

"Roger." Kovac scanned his instruments and read off the slant range. The exchange was rapid, with brief holds for verification.

"Coming on the range," Mallon said.

"I read you as seven degrees east by both timing and radar. Can you give me an inertial check?"

"Seven degrees east . . . check."

"I'm scanning for optical angle. Flash a beam."

"Beam on," Mallon came back.

"Roger, I have you. Optical angle is"—Faulk gazed through the scarred port, wondering if ever again he'd touch the moon. Twice in a lifetime was too much to expect. High adventure came rarely, and to few men; none before him had ever known such as this. What did the future hold? Parades, a brief moment of glory . . . oblivion? Perhaps he'd do his time, retire, take Karen out to California and bask in the sun. *The heck I will.* His lips formed the words. Good astronauts were at a premium. There'd be other vehicles, other missions—"T plus 3 minutes . . ."

Three minutes more of the moon. Kovac's words rang in his mind. Three more minutes, then he'd be just another earthling going home—back to tell the brass and the TV audiences all about it. *Self-glory, Joe?* Not a bit, Doc. Suddenly he knew the denial to be true. He wasn't here for self-glory. If he were, he'd be aching to get back, aching to take his bows and make the lecture circuit. He'd subscribe to a clipping bureau, sell his story to *Life,* give testimonials to breakfast cereals and rake in the chips. But he didn't want that. No, darn it, he wanted this—the moon. The alien feel under his foot, the rock no eye had seen. He remembered reading John Glenn's account of the first sunset seen by an American from space. It had been sheer poetry. Now he knew how Glenn had felt. Something new, that was it. It wasn't the beauty of the sunset; it was the fact that no American eye ever before had beheld such a sunset. Not from space. Like the patch. Not beautiful, certainly. Then what? A small ash-covered plain on a desolate world, no more remarkable than a patch of sand on the Mojave. Except that this was a strange plain nestling the breast of another world. Something new, something different—that's what gave the kicks. Or was it? Perhaps only a handful of men would really understand how he felt. Phil Herndon would. *I envy you, Joe. I really do.* It came to him that the administrator hadn't been referring to the glory he'd reap but to this—the tremendous sense of accomplishment, the self-satisfaction. That's what Herndon meant.

"T plus 2 minutes . . ."

Kovac's voice reminded him of sand pouring through an hourglass. Each grain was a second; now the grains at the top were thinning, rushing into the hole of time: the lower half was history. Only the sand at the top counted, for it represented life. The sand at the bottom was but memory. He looked at the timers: there were seven, each with a different function. Minus time to engine ignition, plus time of engine burn following ignition, coast time in orbit, that marked out ordained segments of life.

He gazed hungrily at the patch. In the dim earthshine he discerned the swath cut by the Bug's exhaust, the boot marks left in the ash, the black ridge on which he had stood looking over the lonely Ocean of Storms. There was the crevice with its magical life. A handful of cells. How had they gotten there? From earth? From some remote corner of the sky? Or had they been created in the changing chemistry of the moon's birth? There was a problem for the eggheads. There'd be hurried huddles, theories, learned papers. A hundred lecture planks would be created overnight. Five thousand professors in five thousand classrooms would smile knowingly and say: *It is evident* . . . But it wasn't evident. Still, where did they come from? *There's life out there, Joe. Life.* Kovac standing, rapt eyes turned upward toward the firmament. That was the main thing. If Max were right. *T plus* . . . He returned his attention to the copilot.

"Optical angle closing," Kovac chanted, sighting through an instrument that measured angular distance from the vertical. Faulk studied the heavens slightly to the east. Within seconds he spotted the beam from Apollo, little more than a bright spot moving among the stars. "Stand by for countdown to optical angle equals zero," the copilot finished.

"Roger, standing by," Mallon called.

"Plus 6 seconds, 5, 4, 3, 2, 1 . . . Mark!" At the instant of time zero he punched a button starting still another timer.

"Mark."

"Optical angle equals zero, vertical range 608,000 feet . . ."

"Roger."

"Orbital speed 5,200 feet per second . . ."

"Roger."

"Time to launch, minus 80 seconds at time hack."

"Standing by . . ."

"Minus 86 seconds, 85, 84, 83, 82, 81, mark!"

"Mark," Mallon replied.

Faulk felt his muscles tighten. Scarcely more than a minute left on the moon. The seconds were flying. *T minus 75, 74, 73* . . . He looked at the controls, studying the positions of the various firing keys, memorizing patterns already so deeply imbedded in his mind that no amount of time would ever erase them. This panel for the reaction engines—one-pound, two-pound, five-pound and fifty-pound jets; gimbaling controls, firing controls, keys for clusters placed fore, aft and around the perimeter. The main engine panel . . .

"T minus 30 seconds," Kovac called.

Faulk gave him a quick glance. He had assumed the now familiar position—body hunched, eyes riveted on his instruments, the remainder of the universe closed out. The red lights reflecting from his helmet gave him a diabolic appearance. The gloved hand resting on the edge of the panel was relaxed.

"T minus 20 seconds . . ."

"Mark—T minus 20," Mallon chanted.

"Pilot report all systems at go," another voice broke in.

Burke! Faulk straightened abruptly, realizing he'd forgotten. "All systems at go," he snapped tersely.

"Roger . . . standing by."

"T minus 10 seconds," Kovac intoned. His voice, rising, held the tight edge of expectancy. ". . . minus 7, 6, 5, 4, 3, 2, 1 . . . zero!"

"Ignition." Faulk punched a button. The roaring came through the floor, deafening after the silence of the moon. "Main engines firing," he called, raising his voice.

"Roger . . ."

"Tremendous vibration . . . feel a stirring. Yes, we're lifting. Have cleared launching cradle. Ash is swirling up . . . blotting out the ports."

"Altitude 10 . . . 15 feet," Kovac interrupted.

"Like launching from the Cape," Faulk sang out. A sudden elation swept him. "We're headed for the old earth barn."

He gave a quick look downward through the side mirror. The ash was roiling in the exhaust so that the surface resembled the uneasy movements of a vast blob of protoplasm. It seemed to rise and fall away, at the same time curving outward like fountain waters. He caught a glimpse of the abandoned launch structure before it vanished behind the dust curtain.

"Altitude 50 feet," Kovac called.

Faulk didn't reply, his eyes were glued to the heavens: the splash of stars, the creamy super highway called the Milky Way. He felt the shift of body fluids as the Bug began its programed pitchover, controlled by the guidance system.

Kovac spoke almost conversationally into the mike: "Coming up for a visit, Dad."

"Could use company," Mallon agreed. "My little cabin in the sky—nice, but it gets lonely."

"Lift-off pictures coming in," Burke broke in. "Saw the beginning of engine firing, then the ash whirling up. Nothing else. Better give us a rundown," he added.

"Roger," Faulk responded, realizing he should have been doing it all along. "We've gone through programed pitchover . . . rising fast. We're on automatic with pilot controlling main engine power. Smooth operation . . . almost no vibration or sensation of movement except for accelerative G."

"Still see the patch?"

"Yes . . . no, I'm not certain. There are a number of ashy areas, all sizes and shapes. The Ocean of Storms is flattening out again. Can't see individual rocks and ridges, but the dark splotches make more sense now. We know they're rock . . . rugged rock. Climbing fast. She's a real going bucket, Whitey."

"Plus 60 seconds," Kovac reported. "Fuel, 80 percent."

"See a crater . . . two craters. They're small, or at least look small. No real way of judging. Light's baffling. Can't see anything that looks like a good landing spot. Everything's beginning to melt now . . . getting back to the black-and-cream pattern."

"Holding Apollo on radar," Kovac declared, as Faulk paused. He raised his head from the cone of red lights. "Maybe we can track optically."

"Try," Burke encouraged.

"Roger."

"I'll flash a beam," Mallon interrupted.

"Do that, Les." Kovac raised his instrument, scrunching his body to see through the port.

"How's the glass?" Burke asked.

"Lousy," Faulk replied. "Didn't know how bad it was till we landed."

"Think you'll have any trouble?"

"In rendezvous? Don't anticipate any. We have a good radar lock-on and if Max gets an optical track—"

"You'll have line-of-sight closure later, that's certain," Burke interrupted.

"Perhaps sooner," Kovac said, without taking his eyes from the instrument. "Beam on, Les?"

"Like a lighthouse in the sky. You should pick it up."

"There's a heavy starfield."

"I'll give you my inertial position . . ."

Faulk leaned to one side, watching the moon while they chattered. Strange, but go-up was coming a lot easier than go-down, at least so far. They hadn't expected that. Max and Les were gossiping as if they were two fighter pilots yakking in formation rather than two astronauts attempting to locate each other in an alien sky. Burke was more at ease also, giving advice and asking questions as if he were monitoring a routine flight. Routine . . . already?

He looked at the land sweeping past below. No longer alien, he believed he discerned patterns in the dim earthshine. Here would be a ridge, there a crater . . . beyond, a plain. Like learning to read an air photo taken from high altitude, he reflected. His eyes dwelt on a knife-edge shadow crossing what appeared to be a large ash-covered plain. A chasm. He saw other smaller shadows, recognizing them as rills—minor cracks that gridded the moon in spots. And some not too minor. Did they, also, contain life? Or was it a phenomenon of a single gulf? He deemed it unlikely, yet how could the spores transfer from chasm to chasm over the vacuum surface? He'd have to think about that. He became aware of Mallon's voice again:

"Better cut for a while," he was saying. "Using too much electricity. We'll try later."

"Okay." Kovac set aside the instrument and dropped his head toward the red lights. "T plus 180 seconds, altitude . . ."

Listening, Faulk had the impression of being hurled through a dark tunnel, a vertiginous feeling he recognized as due to lack of a visual reference. At go-down he'd had the moon. Now, with the moon behind him, he had nothing except a vast sweep of stars glowing fluidly through the blurred port, and off to one side, the slim crescent of earth. Kovac called off altitudes of 25, 30 and 35 thousand feet—time at 200, 230 and 260 seconds. Time versus altitude. On earth it made a nice graph. Here it represented a chunk of metal storming through alien space.

"Velocity 5,250 feet per second," Kovac said, cutting into his thoughts. "Altitude 45,000 . . . time plus 270 seconds. Fuel remaining . . . 11 percent."

Faulk cut in the reaction engines to provide additional control. "Give me a beat count to 300 seconds."

"Roger." Kovac picked up the time from the counter, intoning the seconds. When he reached plus 295 Faulk moved his hand to a switch. ". . . 97, 98, 99, 300."

Faulk cut the main engines. "Engines off." *Roger. Roger.* Voices from two worlds floated in over the phones.

"Altitude 49,000 feet," Kovac reported. He spoke in crisp, mechanical tones. "Speed 5,500 feet per second."

"Using the reaction jets to boost speed for required transfer ellipse," Faulk said. *Roger. Roger.*

"Plus 315 seconds, speed 5,600 feet per second, altitude 50,000 feet." The copilot's voice held satisfaction. "We're at pericynthion."

"Final go-up," Faulk said crisply. "Entering transfer ellipse."

"Computer says you're in the window," Burke advised. "Data looks good. Can you shoot Doc some biomedical readings?"

"Sure." Kovac flipped a switch. "No sweat on blood pressure now. This is a smooth ride, deluxe. All over but the shouting."

"We hope!"

"Tell the girls we're coming home."

"They know, Max."

"Max is right. It looks like a green bird," Faulk broke in. "I'm plenty happy over the way this crate operates, Whitey. Aside from the glass problem and insufficient downward vision—and exhaust glare—the design is sound."

"We'll want every scrap of info, Joe."

"I'd like to see a larger supply of descent fuel," Kovac suggested. "That go-down was hairy."

"The designers are already on that, Max."

"We have plenty of ascent fuel left in the main tank," Faulk commented. "Maybe they could effect a trade-off without adding weight."

"Possibly. How about fuel for the reaction jets?"

"Should have enough. Don't know yet."

"Looks smooth," Burke agreed. "All over but rendezvous and reentry."

"The prodigal sons come home." Mallon sighed. "I knew this was too good to last."

Chapter 12

"Velocity 5,600 feet per second, climb rate 10,000 feet per minute," Kovac announced, "and on two cylinders."

"Poor joke," Mallon commented. "What's your altitude?"

"Passing through 79,000 at"—he switched his glance—"63 west. T plus 10 minutes . . . a few seconds under."

"On the ball. Don't be late for dinner."

"We run on schedule," Kovac retorted.

They talked, comparing data until Burke interrupted, curious about the lands near the moon's western limb.

"See Grimaldi?" he asked.

"Sprawled like a saucer due south of us," Kovac responded. "It's huge, tremendous. Even under the earthshine you can see deep shadows on the west wall. Part of the floor looks glass-smooth but it may be the way the light washes it. The eastern portion's rugged with craters—a No Man's Land."

"Any sign of color?"

"Are you kidding? This is earthshine."

"Thought I'd ask," Burke said. "One of the selenologists thought he detected some."

"His eyes must be better than mine," the copilot declared.

"Probably not as tired."

"At the moment you're right, Whitey. I feel like the lids are full of sand."

Idly watching the moon, Faulk listened. With attitude control on automatic, he leaned back, relaxed, fighting the desire to sleep. With the tremendous power push to maximum velocity behind them, they glided through a velvet sky toward rendezvous, still half a world away. Steered by inertial guidance, the Bug sped toward a remote cube in the sky. Independent of magnetism, radio or earth trackers, the system was self-contained. Its name derived from the inertia of all bodies—the tendency of a body at rest to remain at rest until acted upon by outside forces. In the Bug's case, the outside forces were supplied by the main engines and small reaction jets. Accelerometers attached to a platform gyrostabilized at right angles to the gravitational field measured these forces as units of thrust. Integrated and summed, they yielded a constant readout of the Bug's position. Backed by radar, voice and optical scope, the Bug climbed unerringly into the night-cloaked lunar skies.

The main engines supplemented by the reaction jets had pushed the Bug to a speed leading to a perigee altitude slightly above that of Apollo; now, with no atmosphere to slow it, the Bug raced west across the face of the moon, at the same time spiraling outward toward a rendezvous some fifty minutes in the future. A pleasant, mellow feeling stole through Faulk's body. Like drifting in a gondola along a Venice canal, he supposed. They should have music. Strange, the sands had poured through the hourglass and now the patch was history. A dusty floor, a yawning crevice, a low border of rough rock resembling heaps of jagged anthracite—that about summed up his firsthand knowledge of the new world. A small vacuum plain splashed with earthshine and shadow. And life! Somehow in that barren and remote spot a borderland life clung to the edge of existence at the bottom of a black pit. What was its purpose? Or did life need purpose? He reflected on it. Were the few cells scooped up by Kovac the end of a long evolutionary ladder, dying as the moon died, or were they a beginning? Musingly he watched Grimaldi recede. A crater-strewn plateau raced toward them, visible in the dim earthlight as circular and elliptical daubs.

Kovac interrupted his chatting to say: "Eighty-seven west . . . altitude 142,500 feet at T plus 14 and a few seconds. I see night-night ahead. It resembles an opaque black curtain stretched across the face of the moon."

As he paused, Burke urged, "Keep going. We're taping it, Max. Every bit of information is extremely valuable."

"From an authority on the spot," Kovac agreed.

As he launched into a running description, Faulk watched the black curtain rush toward them. Still far ahead, it came as a wavefront, rolling over and smothering the cream-splashed plains and peaks. Forming an abrupt border—as sharp as the Terminator which separated night from day—it ushered in a part of the moon unlit by either earthshine or sun. This was night-night, the term coined by Kovac to distinguish it from the night lit by the earth's reflected light.

"It's coming faster and faster," Kovac reported. "It's hurtling toward us at fantastic velocity . . . almost overwhelming. Gives me a spooky feeling."

"Not scientific," Mallon cut in. "It looks slower from here . . . somewhat like a tide edging up on a beach."

"Here it comes," Kovac ended.

The black curtain appeared to make a titanic leap forward, speeding under them. The view below was that of a nightmare pit, of nothingness. Faulk stared until his eyes ached. Not till he raised them to the dark horizon slicing through the starfield did he realize the utter blackness below.

With the shoulder of the moon between the Bug and earth and contact lost with Cap. Com, they chatted on and off with Mallon, relaxing as much as their cramped seats would allow. Kovac occasionally transmitted data, verifying slant range and navigational position. But mainly they rested, conscious of the trying period ahead.

During a lull while Faulk was occupied with thoughts of Karen and the kids, Kovac asked thoughtfully, "Now that it's almost over, would you do it again, Joe?"

Caught by surprise, he deliberated, aware of the other's scrutiny. "Yes, I would," he said finally, wondering at his own hesitancy. "So would you."

"I'm not certain."

"They couldn't hold you back, Max."

"I suppose." Kovac watched him pensively. "Anything after this will be anticlimactic—a real letdown."

He's right, Faulk reflected, the future was downhill. This was the peak, the big adventure, the never-to-be-equaled period of their lives. Did old astronauts, like old soldiers, merely fade away? Or could this be the threshold? He tentatively said, "There's Mars . . ."

"We'll be too old for Mars," Kovac retorted impatiently. "That's for the new breed. Damned if I want to wind up running a shuttle to orbit . . . delivering groceries to space stations."

Faulk contemplated it. He could see his point, exactly. Each major breakthrough was followed by a lull while they prepared for the next hurdle; and during the lull the successors came—young, eager men, crowding the older ones aside. The latter became the caretakers—instructors, advisers, consultants to the industries building the vehicles. That's how it had been. But it needn't be. He wasn't old. Neither was Kovac nor Mallon. Perhaps they would be when Mars came along, and Venus; but what of the moon? They'd need pilots and navigators, more than they'd ever hope to get. Driving a bus into orbit was one thing; driving it to the Sea of Rains or the flat plains of the Sea of Crises was something quite different. It wasn't like pushing a hack. Not even Max could claim that.

"There's still plenty to do," he finally said.

"My prime drive isn't to *do,* it's to *see,*" Kovac observed. "In that respect, I'm more like an explorer."

Faulk raised his eyes interestedly. "That doesn't tie in with your background, Max—your flying."

"Planes take you places, Joe."

"That's part of it," he admitted.

"Maybe I'm getting mellow," Kovac mused.

"A letdown. We've been pushing too hard."

"Yeah." He managed a grin. "We'd better not let down now."

"Amen." Faulk chuckled appreciatively.

In the silence that followed, Kovac gazed out the port. He'd been given a rare insight into the copilot, Faulk realized. It was a part of Max he'd never seen before. Perhaps no one had, unless it were Eve. Max, a man who played his emotions close to his vest, had a reputation as iron-nerved, emotionless, operating with machine precision. A dark stoic face and fathomless eyes gave him a cold, tough appearance. When he considered it, that was precisely the picture he held of the man; there was little in their relationship to indicate otherwise. Kovac, Burke, Waco, Myers—these were men of a breed, latter-day Glenns, Carpenters and Schirras. Max was right. They were a strange mixture of engineer, pilot, adventurer and explorer.

But Kovac *was* iron-nerved, he *did* operate with machine precision, and almost invariably his responses *were* quick and correct. But behind the mask lurked another Kovac—a man who wondered, who held dreams.

What of himself? What did Kovac see when he looked at him? What did Mallon see? Burke or Herndon? Not what was deep within him, certainly. They saw only the surface, the mask he presented to the world. The rest was too intimate. Only Karen penetrated the mask—knew the stirrings and hungers and hopes, and even there he had secret dreams. People generally accepted the mask as the real person, like judging the merchandise of a store by its showcase. He did the same. Like his picture of Les Mallon. He resurrected it in his mind—the wiry blond hair, lopsided smile, ready jest. He associated him with parties, good times and girls. At the same time he recognized that as the façade Mallon had built, carefully and purposefully, without pretense. Or was this, also, camouflage? Was Les really the gay, carefree, devil-may-care person he seemed? That's how he was accepted. Clown, a ladies' man, a *bon vivant* who also happened to be a damned good astronaut. What did the laugh and jest conceal? Did he hunger inside? And for what?

"Coming 'round the mountain, coming 'round the mountain," Mallon sang. "I can see the dawn line . . . a rope of pearls around a lovely lady's throat."

"I read us at 162 west," Kovac said. "Altitude 397,500 feet at T plus 40 minutes."

"Slant range 393,000 feet," Mallon confirmed.

"Check, we're overhauling you, Dad."

"Good to see the sun flooding over the plain," Mallon said. "That black was too black. A few more days and I'll be lapping it up on the beach, improving my tan."

"You'll be in a clinic somewhere, is what you mean," Kovac

corrected. "The medics and headshrinkers will want to squeeze you dry for a few weeks first."

"Why me? I didn't land on the moon," Mallon protested. "No germs in me."

"The solitude—they'll want to see how much it's warped you."

"They'll find a superman," Mallon predicted.

Faulk watched through the port while Mallon and Kovac exchanged navigational data. All at once he saw a white thread arcing across the glass; it thickened rapidly.

"See the dawn line," he announced. He ceased speaking, studying the port. The thread was wavery, not too sharp, which he realized was due to the blurred condition of the glass. The following thought was that it was much worse. "How are your ports, Les?"

"Lousy," Mallon responded cheerfully, "or else I need an ophthalmologist. They ought to hang shielding over the glass . . . open it only when you need it. How's the Bug?"

"About the same. I'm watching the dawn line come up. It's pretty blurry."

"Bats make out, and look at them."

"We'll make out," Faulk asserted. "They should change the system on the next rig though. This is for the birds."

"I'm making notes for a new design now—the Mallon De Luxe Spaceship. It'll have a stewardess."

"Just one?" Kovac mocked.

"More on the larger models," Mallon replied urbanely. "A real stimulus to space travel."

They exchanged banter for a while, then Kovac said, "Okay, Dad, let's get with it. We're crossing 168 east at 495,000 feet . . . T plus 51 minutes."

"Check, I have you on the scope."

"Optical?"

"And radar both. Here's the slant range and closure rate . . ."

While they exchanged information, Faulk pondered about the

ports. They were still okay for rendezvous, although they might cause trouble during final closure, a damned ticklish maneuver. And they'd probably give trouble during earth reentry. Les was right, they needed redesign—some method of protecting the glass when not in use. He'd noted other necessary improvements—better downward vision, more maneuvering fuel for landing on alien surfaces, more preflight information on the nature of selected landing areas. The latter meant more instruments soft-landed ahead of time. He let his mind wander. Mars . . . Kovac was right. It still lay too far in the future for him. But they'd scarcely scratched the moon. What would it be like to land on Mare Imbrium or the Sea of Crises, the beautiful elliptical plain lying near the moon's eastern limb? He'd be back—the knowledge came with a flash of insight. He had no doubt it was true. Whitey'd take the next mission. They'd want one experienced hand along—probably Les, he surmised. But he and Max might catch the follow-on, perhaps inside of a year. . . .

"Dawn coming in like a snow avalanche," Kovac observed. He flicked his eyes to the board. "I read us at 150 east, altitude 542,000."

"You read right," Mallon confirmed.

"I'll try the optical scope."

"Give us your closure rate first," Mallon suggested. "Let's check it."

"Roger." They began comparing figures.

"Any word from Cap. Com?" Faulk asked when they were finished.

"A few garbled words. These relay satellites aren't so hot," Mallon answered.

"Let me know when you hear."

"Will do. I predict they'll have a full house down there for this one."

"Likely," Faulk agreed.

They discussed closure proceedings briefly, then Kovac gave their longitude as 139 east, with altitude at 597,000 feet. T plus 59.

"We're going over the top," he told Mallon. "Have you in the visual scope."

Making a quick check of instruments and controls, Faulk turned his attention to the port. The dawn line raced toward them and in another moment raced by below. Kovac announced altitude at 611,000 feet with speed at 5,600 feet per second.

"This is a real space buggy," he finished.

"What's your lead angle, Buster?" Kovac gave it. Listening, Faulk felt a quiet contentment. The hellish go-up was proving a breeze. They practically had it made.

Les Mallon didn't mind the solitude. He liked cutting through the stark lunar skies, sensing the peace and quiet of complete isolation. Aside from the low hum of the air fan and occasional cracklings and voices on the radio, it was a world of absolute stillness. He came to know intimately places with such haunting names as the Sea of Vapors, Seething Bay and the Marsh of Sleep, just as he came to know the sweep of the Haemus Mountains overlooking the Sea of Serenity and the Disneyland of craters east of the Foaming Sea. He saw the moon as a never-never land of enchanting wonders.

During the brief span of daylight he could chat with Joe, Max and Whitey. Or just talk, describing the strange contours of the moon in minute detail. It gave him immense satisfaction that Cap. Com taped every word—that it would become part of a lunar bible for future astronauts.

He especially liked the short, dark nights. That was a time of complete peace and solitude. Occasionally he napped briefly; more often he gazed through blurred ports at the wondrous expanse of the firmament, dreaming of things warm in memory. Somehow whirling through the lunar nights recalled long-ago years with the

Navy, when he'd flown the old Demons and Tiger Cats. Roaring off the carriers at night, speeding over the Pacific—those were the good memories. He liked the carriers.

Somewhere along the line he'd been sidetracked—assigned as a test pilot to newer and hotter jets. And when the Navy needed representation in NASA's growing manned space program, he'd been a logical choice. He didn't regret it, but at times he did miss the excitement of coming in for a night landing on the rolling decks, or hurtling through the skies in a simulated attack mission.

Yet this was better. Like now. Sky and moon were black, fantastically black, and somewhere in the blackness the Moon Bug hurtled toward him. This time the picture was reversed. Apollo was a carrier on an orbital sea, the Bug a hot jet coming in to land. Although he didn't have the exhilaration of wind whistling over the canopy and the harsh jet whine, he had the thrill of guiding it home. Joe and Max—good fellows. He suspected that Joe probably was the better pilot, but you couldn't beat Max when it came to instruments. Joe's confidence lay in his own abilities; Max's in the ability he accorded the little black boxes. That was the difference as he saw it.

Faceplate open, relaxed, he let the thoughts drift through his mind between gossiping and exchanging data with Max. A long way from Santa Ana, he mused. The pleasant southern California city where he'd spent his boyhood had receded to a remote memory. He remembered the surfing and fishing, all right, and night bonfires along the beach. The banker's daughter—what was her name? Donna, that was it. But he remembered the jets better—how he used to bicycle out to El Toro and watch the F8Fs and F7Us thunder from the strip. That had decided him. The radio burped and Kovac came on. The Bug was near now.

"This is a real space buggy," Kovac was saying.

Mallon grinned. "What's your lead angle, Buster?" Kovac gave

it and he relaxed again. He was watching the instruments when
the red light flashed.

Flashed violently.

"Ready for final move-in," Faulk said, conscious they hadn't
heard from Les for several moments. When Mallon failed to respond, he called sharply: "Come in, Apollo." He sat straighter,
feeling an odd tingling. Kovac gave him a quick, covert glance.
"Apollo. Calling Apollo!" Faulk's voice held a tense edge.

"Clowning," Kovac snapped irritably.

"No one's clowning," Faulk rebuked. "Come in, Apollo . . .
Apollo." The silence that answered him sent a chill through his
bones.

"Trouble with the radio?" Kovac suggested. His flat tone denied
the possibility.

"Don't believe so," he replied tightly. He raised his voice: "Come
in, Apollo."

"Damn funny. What could happen?" Kovac asked. "He was
there a moment ago."

"What's our position?"

"Just crossed 131 east . . . apogee at 611,000," Kovac quickly
answered.

"Range?"

"Eighty thousand feet."

Faulk calculated quickly. "Not too bad. How's fuel?"

Kovac glanced at the gauges. "Reaction control tank . . .
3 percent."

"Not good."

"Nurse it," the copilot urged.

"Will do," Faulk promised. He spoke louder. "Calling Apollo.
Come in, Apollo." A vast silence came from space. They exchanged
quick glances, struck by the same thought. If something had hap-

pened to Mallon, they couldn't enter Apollo—not with the airlock secured from the inside.

"We should be hearing from Burke." Kovac's voice held an uncertain quality as if he couldn't quite decipher the situation.

"Pretty quick," he agreed. "We'll have to close by line of sight."

"Roger." Kovac gave their coordinates, range, required velocity changes and closure speeds in a voice that said he was frankly relieved that a decision had been made.

Faulk shut out all thought of Apollo, or what they might find when they got there, concentrating on the ticklish task at hand. Apollo traveled in an orbital plane 3,000 feet below them—too many miles behind! He would have to slow the Bug through a series of delicate maneuvers . . . dropping to the lower orbital plane within intercept distance of the other vehicle. He corrected attitude, conscious of their scant fuel, then gimbaled a cluster of small jets in the direction of their flight path and fired them.

Kovac, his eye to the scope, said: "She's tumbling, a slow tumble."

Faulk didn't respond. This was the time they needed Les—to hold Apollo's attitude stable, to verify navigational data with Apollo's onboard computer and batteries of instruments. But they didn't have Les, had nothing but their eyes, his skill at the controls . . . a handful of fuel.

"I read us at slightly under 611,000 feet," Kovac said.

Faulk shifted, searched the sky and finally spotted Apollo from the glint on its sunstruck side. It looked small and far away, like a piece of driftwood in the expanse of an ocean. Moving in a slow tumble, the reflected light constantly changed. Faulk piloted the Bug intuitively, deliberately falling behind the clock—trading time for accuracy in an effort to conserve every ounce of fuel. The radio crackled and Burke came on. Faulk tersely explained the situation.

"Bad," Burke said grimly. "Let me flash the word."

The radio fell silent. Faulk and Kovac discussed the problem of docking, more, Faulk thought, to occupy time than to reach a solution. In a few moments Burke was back.

"Waco and Myers are here," he said. "They flew in last night."

"Hi, Johnny . . . Gary."

"Hiya, Joe—"

"Herndon's on the way over," Burke cut in. "What's your present status and position?"

Kovac filled him in, detailing the problems they might encounter.

"Here's Herndon with Chappel from engineering," Burke interrupted.

"Hello, Joe . . . Max," Phil Herndon greeted. "We have a problem."

"You're telling us," Faulk drily said. "We topped with a pretty long lead. We're dropping to a lower orbit."

"How's your fuel?"

"Over 2 percent," Kovac cut in.

"We'll have to talk turkey," Herndon said, "put it on the line. Chappel doesn't believe it's radio trouble."

"Neither do we. Les would flash a search beam."

"Exactly. He also ruled out explosion."

"Not likely," Faulk agreed.

"Have you gotten a good look at Apollo?"

"It's in slow tumble, Phil."

"We were afraid of that. It'll make docking tough. We'll have to assume Les is dead . . . or completely disabled."

"We've assumed that."

"How about a tether rope, Joe?" It took him a moment to recognize the voice as Waco's.

"Hi, Johnny," he greeted. "We've thought of that. We'll have to wait and see, size up the situation. If we can get a line to Apollo, we can pull these crates together."

"You'll have to get close."

"I believe we can."

"Watch for ramming," Waco warned. "If that baby's swinging—"

He didn't finish. Herndon broke in briskly: "We see two vital problems—docking with Apollo in tumble, and entry."

"We'll tough the entry end out when we get there," Faulk decided. "Right now I'm going to concentrate on closing . . . docking."

"Chappel's standing by if you need engineering advice."

He didn't say so, but Faulk considered any advice from Chappel useless. If they had to force entry into Apollo, they would damage it irreparably for earth reentry.

In the pause that followed, Kovac asked flat-voiced, "Could he send us a blowtorch?"

Herndon disregarded the question. "Keep in touch, every move. Burke will monitor you."

"Roger," Faulk responded. "Our retrofire will take us through Apollo's orbital plane with about a 10,000-foot lead."

"Too much," Burke cut in.

"Can't be helped. We haven't enough fuel for maneuver. We'll have to drop speed—fall back and allow Apollo to overtake us, then accelerate . . . overhaul it."

"It's delicate, Joe."

"What isn't?" As the silence came, he glanced at the copilot and cut in the jets, firing a brief burst.

Kovac called 609,000 feet and, finally, 608,000 feet. "Range is 9,750 feet," he finished.

"Speed?"

"Below 5,100 . . . by a hair."

"Roger." Faulk craned his head, studying Apollo briefly before turning back to the controls. He made several minor adjustments, acutely aware of the cost in fuel.

"We're dropping faster." Kovac leaned closer to the instruments. "Near 607,000. Range is shortening."

Faulk gimbaled another light jet and fired a staccato burst, wait-

ing, all at once conscious of the silence. Burke, Waco, Herndon—
they were waiting. Waiting helplessly. Apollo, now traveling over
100 feet per second faster than the Bug, would overtake them in little over a minute. If he accelerated a few seconds ahead of time,
he'd be moving too fast for final closure. It struck him that this was
a problem in aviation similar to flying trick formations. He'd have
to go by seat-of-the-pants.

After moments that seemed hours Kovac said, "Altitude
606,000. Apollo overhead."

Faulk twisted his body to look. His first glimpse was of a dot of
light that gradually lengthened, then shortened again. It took him
an instant to recognize it as the effect of sunlight falling on the
vehicle's shifting surfaces as it tumbled slowly around its longitudinal axis.

"Lord," he exclaimed softly, "it's turning cartwheels in the sky."
He had a quick image of attempting to dock with the swinging
nose; it could crush the Bug like an eggshell.

Kovac broke the silence: "One percent fuel."

His words had the ring of doom.

Chapter 13

"Getting there," Kovac breathed, staring through the port. He
had ceased calling off speed, range and closure rate, aware that
Faulk was flying a line-of-sight approach, disregarding the information of dials and gauges.

Faulk gave a scarcely perceptible nod, his eyes glued to the other
vehicle. Suddenly it had grown enormous. Its tumbling motion alternately showed it end-on and as a vertical shaft in the sky, making
distances deceptive. The blurred glass gave it a freckled out-of-

focus appearance. Rising fast, they climbed a few hundred feet above it—dropped slowly and passed through the 608,000-foot orbital plane as Apollo edged ahead again.

"Fuel . . . near zero," Kovac said tonelessly.

Faulk touched the thrusters, correcting attitude and velocity. Whirling along like a two-car train, a scant hundred yards separated the vehicles. The fogged view bothered him. Apollo's lines were indistinct, giving the impression of an out-of-focus photograph. He paused, evaluating his next move. It sounded simple. All he had to do was speed up or slow down, according to their relative positions. But it didn't work that way. A change of speed also brought a change of orbit. He couldn't reach Apollo by going in a straight line, for in orbit there are no straight lines. Apollo was moving in a giant curve; to reach it he must travel in a curve. He had to bend his path by firing rockets vertically to their flight path—exerting just enough force to maintain altitude while other jets exerted push along the curved path of orbit. And he had to approach close, yet not so close that the rotating vehicle would strike them. With near zero fuel . . .

He spoke quietly into the mike: "Beginning final closure . . ."

"Roger," Burke said tersely. "Vision okay?"

"Pretty bad. Can't see detail."

"Don't get too close."

"No choice, Whitey. If we gotta rope that baby . . ."

"Okay, Joe. Easy does it. Keep us plugged in."

"Will do."

Faulk gimbaled a small one-pound jet at the stern and pointing another vertically into the sky, fired them briefly. Apollo swam toward them, at the same time dropping. He made several minor corrections, watching the other vehicle intently. The march of inches—it drew closer and closer. They moved in a vast silence, so still that Faulk fancied he could hear the blood coursing through his veins, the dull thudding beat of his heart. The copilot, tense and expectant, kept his eyes riveted to the fuel gauge. His world had closed down—now centered around a slender needle falling slowly to a point marked zero. Tougher than go-down. The thought flashed through Faulk's mind. The landing had been so action-filled that he hadn't time to consider danger. But here, watching Apollo, waiting . . .

"Zero fuel," Kovac called. "We're holding almost steady."

"Fuel reads zero," Faulk reported, without moving his eyes from Apollo's burn chamber. It came down in a slow ponderous sweep, passed the port by a dozen yards and receded. As the vehicle passed through the vertical, the nose swung into view, light glints reflecting from the dark ports.

"Lifeless as a tomb," Kovac stated somberly.

Lifeless as a tomb. The words echoed in Faulk's mind. Apollo, space, the moon's bleak surface—all were lifeless. A realm of silence, of death. Man . . . the intruder. He eyed the tumbling hulk speculatively. If he could . . . He turned decisively, instructing, "Vent the cabin air, open the hatch and secure one end of line. We'll have to work fast."

"Roger." As the copilot turned to the task, he outlined his plan on the radio.

A quick exchange followed at Cap. Com before Burke replied: "Best bet is to loop the line over the cluster of jets near Apollo's airlock. Chappel says it should hold."

"*Should?*"

"You have no alternative, Joe."

"Will do."

Faulk pushed himself from the seat. Partially obscured by the edge of the port, the burn chamber came around again a scant half-dozen yards away. He realized the Bug was moving slowly in yaw and started to counter it—the jet didn't fire.

"Zero fuel," he said bleakly.

Burke asked worriedly, "Range?"

"Half a dozen yards. We're in slight yaw. We'd better get at it." He rose abruptly and made a slipknot in the line, looping it around his shoulder while Kovac opened the hatch. The copilot eyed the line protestingly. "It's my baby. No time to argue," Faulk told him.

"Okay, Joe." Kovac grimly took stock of the line. "Let's hope it's heavy enough."

"Take up the slack as soon as I fasten it . . . keep it from jerking," he instructed. "If we handle it right . . ."

"I'll take care of this end," Kovac promised.

Faulk took a forward step, looking down toward the moon, then jolted the edge of the hatch sharply with his shoulder to counter the yawing motion. "If I miss—"

"I'll haul you back," the copilot rapped out sharply. "Watch your faceplate. That steel's hard."

He didn't answer, calculating the swing of Apollo's nose. It came around in a slow arc, sweeping across the face of the moon, climbing toward the stars. Poised, knees slightly flexed, he waited, conscious that the reaction force from the leap could alter the Bug's orbital path. Apollo was like a baton twirled in slow motion, but because of its length, the nose traveled deceptively fast. It came scudding toward him. Crouching, he sprang upward at an angle calculated to allow the vehicle to come up under him, thus lessening the force of impact.

Plunging through space, he had the eerie sensation of a lone swimmer who suddenly discovers himself beyond sight of land. Stars swam across his faceplate in a sky that appeared suddenly blacker. Squirming, he looked down, saw sunglint on the ports rising to meet him. They appeared to move fast. He flexed his legs in time to absorb the impact, lost balance and sprawled in slow motion toward the end of the nose.

"Hang on!" Kovac's voice rang quick alarm in his ears.

Scrambling to his side, he grasped one of the small jet nozzles, having difficulty with the glove. Breathing heavily, he pulled the loop from his shoulder and slipped it over the bell-shaped tube. Kovac, braced against the side of the hatch, pulled the line taut, allowing it to slip through his gloves in an attempt to slow Apollo's swing. As the line came to an end, Faulk felt a sudden jerk. Looking back, he saw the Bug yawing at the end of the tether.

"Nice going," Kovac exulted. "A real ballerina."

He didn't answer. Lying still while he caught his breath, he looked down on the face of the moon. *Apollonius, Condorcet, the Foaming Sea*—his mind registered the fact that less than fifteen minutes had elapsed since the abrupt silence from Mallon. Les! He was inside, somewhere beneath the steel plating. He forcibly dismissed the thought, taking in his own situation. Kovac's braking action on the rope and the sharp jerk as it reached full-length had changed Apollo's rotation to a wobbling motion on its axis, with the nose swinging in small circles. Each swing alternately loosened and tightened the line, resulting in a series of jerks that constantly changed the attitude of both Apollo and the Bug.

"I'll work around to the airlock," Faulk advised; "see if I can get inside."

"Careful, you'll have no line," Kovac warned.

"See if you can pull us closer."

"Will do."

As he began tugging on the line, Faulk studied the slope of the hull. Slanting forward, it fell into an abyss of nothingness; far below he saw the Sea of Fertility, crater Gutenberg, the Marsh of Sleep. The familiar contours renewed his confidence. This no longer was an alien world. He had touched it, existed briefly on its surface, and now was traveling through its skies. Relinquishing his hold on the line, he let his body float a few inches above the steel siding. Strange, although whirling through orbit at 5,200 feet per second, he felt absolutely no sensation of motion. Of course there could be none with no atmosphere, he reflected, and yet he found it difficult to adjust to. Man was used to stresses and strains—without them he felt lost. Gauging Apollo's nose, he pushed gently against the jet nozzle and floated toward it, and a few seconds later grasped the edge of the airlock.

"All right?" Kovac anxiously asked.

He gave a terse answer, swinging his body into the opening. Fumblingly, he pulled the light from his belt and flashed it on the hatch. Wheeling, he took a step forward, facing the Bug: "Airlock open," he rasped tightly. "I'm going in."

"Roger." The copilot sounded vastly relieved. "I'll pull us into docking position."

Faulk turned without answering and pushed against the hatch, encountering unexpected resistance. Exerting more force, he opened it several inches wider. The flash beam revealed part of a space suit. Lord—Mallon! He renewed his efforts until he could step inside. A glance told him the story. Les, his faceplate open, had unlocked the hatch in his last dying seconds. That he had done so without pressurizing his suit was suicide; it also indicated a sudden and grave emergency. What emergency? He looked around intently. Ports, bulkheads, flooring—everything appeared intact. Examining the oxygen valves, he found them closed by the automatic emergency shutoff, a system actuated by sudden loss of pressure.

He reported his finding to Kovac, adding, "I'm going to close the hatch . . . pressurize."

"Meteorite?"

"Looks that way. Les must have been caught with his faceplate open."

"He could have shut it," Kovac objected. "That would have been quicker than opening the hatch. Besides, the hatch was suicide."

"Perhaps he only had time for one decision."

"Meaning?"

"When he realized the air was venting . . ." Faulk paused,

thinking how it must have been. "If he took time to pressurize his suit and didn't make it . . ."

"We'd be dead," Kovac said softly.

"That's about it. He gambled on giving us a chance, Max."

"Les would."

"Yes, he would . . . did." Turning back into the cabin, he looked at the prone figure on the floor; gently he closed the mask to conceal the popped eyes. Hatch closed, he opened an oxygen valve, his eyes on an indicator. The needle remained at zero. That was the story, he thought dully. In the immensity of space, Apollo had crossed paths with a meteorite. He imagined the way it must have been. The air had vented so quickly that Mallon's first indication had been a flashing red light, a sudden light-headedness, a dizziness. His first reaction—and his last—had been to open the airlock.

Returning to the hatch, Faulk said tonelessly, "Meteorite—can't hold cabin pressure."

"Much damage?" Kovac asked quickly.

"Can't tell . . . but enough. We'll have to find it . . . fix it."

"Let's dock." All at once Kovac's voice grew urgent. "Grab the line." Faulk braced himself in the airlock and pulled, exerting a steady pressure. Yawing slightly, the Bug commenced to draw closer. "Easy, easy does it," Kovac cautioned, watching the latching mechanisms move toward each other. Timing Apollo's swinging movements, Faulk gave a final pull—the Bug's nose poked into the docking slip, followed by a series of slight jars. Kovac checked the latching mechanism, then straightening slowly, looked past Faulk's shoulder into Apollo's cabin.

"It's not like coming home," he said. "It's not at all like I thought it'd be."

"No, it's not like coming home." Sensing the other's mood, Faulk added crisply: "We'd better check the damage, get shipshape."

Kovac forced a smile. "Okay, Joe, let's find the hole, seal it. We've got things to do."

They buried Les Mallon in space.

Last rites were held as the Moon Bug and Apollo, linked together, hurtled over the highlands of the Sinus Medii, headed into the Ocean of Storms. *Oceanus Procellarum*—the name Mallon had described as music.

Lester Mallon wasn't alone in death.

With several orbital periods to make preparations, Whitey Burke, Johnny Waco, Gary Myers, Doc Ashfield and Phil Herndon attended his last services. Standing with a crowd of others in the control room at Cape Canaveral, they listened with bowed heads as over 240,000 miles away an astronaut went to final rest, interred in the midst of the great space he had dedicated his life to conquer. The President and the heads of state heard the funeral rites. So did princes and paupers, and millions of just folks. Among them were Karen Faulk and Eve Kovac. Lily Jordan followed it on the radio. When it was over, she bowed her head and cried.

. . . *Because man goeth to his long home, and the mourners go about the streets.*

Joseph Faulk stood in the airlock, facing into the Moon Bug where Les Mallon's body reposed in the pilot's seat. He stood erect, as if bareheaded and facing into a wind, his words strangely muted in the narrow confines. Max Kovac stood at his shoulder, his lips moving silently.

Then shall the dust return to the earth as it was: and the spirit shall return unto God who gave it.

Faulk paused and lowered his voice: "Let us pray."

Afterward they secured the airlock and retreated to Apollo. Faulk moved wordlessly into the pilot's seat. With Lansberg Crater fleeing beneath them, he pushed a button; a small actuator thrust the Moon Bug free.

Kovac broke the silence. "It's where he'd want to be, circling the moon."

"Les would like that."

Yes, Les would like that, he reflected—not moldy ground but space. He'd have the sun, earth and stars for company, and the moon he'd come to know so well. He thought it fitting that the first astronaut who died in deep space should have as a coffin a spaceship—that he should go through eternity circling the world he had come to conquer. Somehow he didn't think Les Mallon would be lonely. Actuating the separation system, he applied a brief burst of power from the reaction jets and watched the Moon Bug gradually fall to the rear. Kovac watched stoically, his eyes hard. Faulk turned from the glass.

"We'd better start checking, get our data for the computer," he said. "It's a long way home."

Crossing the Terminator into the lunar night, he looked back. Far behind, the Moon Bug glinted in the last rays of the sun. Then it too was engulfed by night.

The earth is a small planet, yet huge when compared with the silvery satellite which encircles it. Its volume is over fifty times and its mass over eighty times as great. It is the strong pull of earth which holds the moon in its orbit. Because of this pull, an object breaking free of the moon's gravity and caught by the earth accelerates faster and faster. It reaches the earth traveling at unbelievable speed.

Apollo was one such object. It reached the earth on the third day; or rather the high fringes of earth, where there are only lonely molecules.

"Prepared for reentry," Faulk announced, conscious of a tiredness that permeated every pore of his body.

"We need a check." Burke's voice with its familiar expectancy and tautness filled the cabin.

"Ready for check." Kovac leaned forward, studying the instruments. As Burke went through the list, he answered question by question. And the last question:

"Speed?" The copilot didn't look at the instruments this time; he didn't have to. He knew it by heart.

"Thirty-three thousand miles per hour," he said.

Thirty-three thousand miles per hour. The figure seeped through Faulk's tired mind. Almost twice as fast as reentry from earth orbit; twice as fast as any manned vehicle ever before had entered the earth's air ocean. Yet at the moment, weary with a fatigue that pervaded mind and body, he found the statistic meaningless. He forced himself to review the moments ahead. He had to hit an exact window. A shade too much nose-down pitch and they'd burn like a blazing meteorite; an equal error in nose-up pitch and they'd scream off the top of the air ocean—go into perpetual orbit around the sun.

Les Mallon around the moon; Joe Faulk and Max Kovac around the sun. He shook aside the thought, knowing the toughest part was yet to come. There were grave dangers, almost too much to contemplate. The fringes of outer space were not uniform. There were peaks and valleys, density differences, hundred-mile-per-hour winds at times blowing vertically. This was the realm of the fast check, the reliance on instruments whose sensors ranged far ahead, reporting the state of the air rim.

A quick look at the instruments told him they had done everything they could do; now it lay in other hands. Kovac caught his glance and forced a smile. "Almost there, Joe."

He nodded. The first of the turbulence came, a growing force.

"I'm coming home, Karen." His lips silently formed the words. They'd make it. He had infinite faith in that.

Closing his eyes, he waited.